WANDERING

——BRUSH AND PEN
IN PHILOSOPHICAL REFLECTION

倪培民　Ni Peimin

史地文　Stephen Rowe

 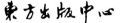东方出版中心　　 Art Media Resources, Ltd.

圖書在版編目（CIP）數據

筆墨哲思游/（美）倪培民，史地文（Stephen Rowe）著.—上海：東方出版中心，2002.9

ISBN 7－80627－945－8

Ⅰ.筆… Ⅱ.①倪…②史… Ⅲ.①漢字－書法－作品集－中國－現代②散文詩－作品集－美國－現代－英文 Ⅳ.①J 292.28②I 712.25

中國版本圖書館 CIP 數據核字（2002）第 061545 號

封面題詞：陳佩秋
Chinese title calligraphy：Chen Peiqiu
責任編輯：吳　迪
edited by Wu Di

Jointly published by
Orient Publishing Center
335 Xianxia Road
Shanghai, China 200336
Tel：0086－21－62597024
Fax：0086－21－62597024
Email：orientpc@sohu.com

and

Art Media Resources, Ltd.
1507 South Michigan Avenue
Chicago, IL 60605 USA
Tel：312－663－5351
Fax：312－663－5177
Email：info@artmediaresources.com
Web：www.artmediaresources.com

本書由中美兩家出版社──東方出版中心和 Art Media Resources，Ltd. 聯合出版。

筆墨哲思游

出版發行：東方出版中心	印　刷：上海精英彩色印務有限公司
地　址：上海市仙霞路 335 號	開　本：889×1194 毫米 1/16
電　話：62417400	印　張：7.5
郵政編碼：200336	版　次：2002 年 9 月第 1 版第 1 次印刷
經　銷：新華書店上海發行所	ISBN 7－80627－945－8/J·22

Etymological meanings of the Chinese word for "wandering" — 游 (*you*):

❶ wandering, excursion

❷ joy, happiness

❸ places of interest

❹ come and go

❺ friendship, relationship

❻ lobbying, persuasion

作者简介　　**About the Authors**

倪培民出生于上海，復旦大學哲學學士、碩士，美國康州大學哲學博士，曾先後在美國三一學院、蒙塔那州立大學任客座教授，并獲杰出教師獎。倪培民現任美國密西根大河谷州立大學哲學系教授，"中外比較哲學叢書"主編，若干哲學學術刊物的編委，以及華東理工大學榮譽教授。他還曾擔任北美中國哲學家協會會長，美國西密西根華人協會會長和中文學校校長。其著作包括英文的《論孔子》、《論銳德》，中文的《托馬斯·銳德》及幾十篇中英文哲學學術論文。
<nip@gvsu.edu>

Ni Peimin was born in Shanghai. He received his B.A. and M.A. from Fudan University in China and Ph.D. from the University of Connecticut. Ni was a visiting professor at Trinity College and Montana State University (where he was awarded for his outstanding teaching), and is now Professor of Philosophy at Grand Valley State University in Michigan, chief editor of a book series, "Chines and Comparative Philosophy," editorial board member for a couple of academic journal, and honorary professor of East China University of Science and Technology. He was formerly President of the Association of West Michigan, and Principal of its affiliated Chinese Language School. Ni's publication includes, in addition to numerous papers, two books in English, *On Confucius,* and *On Reid,* and one in Chinese, *Thomas Reid.* <nip@gvsu.edu>

Stephen Rowe is Professor of Philosophy and Chair of the Philosophy Department at Grand Valley State University in Michigan, and an award winning teacher. His previous works include *Rediscovering The West* (published in Chinese as well as English), *The Vision Of William James,* and a verse book (with photographer David Lubbers) entitled *Abiding: Landscape Of The Soul.* He has lectured in China at East China Normal University and Fudan University. His newest book (forthcoming) is *Living Philosophy: Remaining Awake And Moving Toward Maturity In Complicated Times.* <rowes@gvsu.edu>

史地文是美國密西根大河谷州立大學哲學系教授、系主任，杰出教學獎獲得者。他發表過的著作包括《再看西方》（英文和中文版）、《威廉·詹姆士的視野》，以及一部以散文詩配攝影家大衛·樂博施攝影作品的著作：《恒居——心靈之景》。他曾應邀在復旦大學和華東師範大學作演講。他最近的著作是《活的哲學——在繁雜的時代中保持清醒并走向成熟》。
<rowes@gvsu.edu>

目錄   **CONTENTS**

作者簡介　**About the Authors**

代序：東西方對話談　**Perspectives on East-West Dialogue**

書法與哲理詩　**Calligraphy and Philosophical Verses**

作者的解讀　Interpretive Statements

2

代序：東西方對話談

PERSPECTIVES ON EAST–WEST DIALOGUE

Tu Weiming 杜維明

One of the World's foremost exponents of Confucian tradition and Chinese culture studies, Director of Harvard-Yenching Institute, Harvard-Yenching Professor of Chinese History, Philosophy, and Confucian Studies, Chairman of the Committee on the Study of Religion at Harvard University, and a Fellow of the American Academy of Arts and Sciences. His many books include Confucian Thought: Selfhood As Creative Transformation (1985), Centrality And Commonality: An Essay On Confucian Religiousness (1989), and Way, Learning, And Politics: Essays On The Confucian Intellectual (1993).

當代世界著名的儒家傳統和中國文化研究的代表者之一，美國哈佛大學燕京學院主任，哈佛燕京中國歷史、哲學、暨儒家研究教授，哈佛大學宗教研究委員會主席，美國藝術和科學院院士。

"We must transcend the particular to reach the general; only through the general, can we hope to attain the universal." The quest for universality, so conceived, compels us to overcome concrete particularity so that we can grasp the abstract universal. A case in point is the practitioners of universal ethics' decision to offer the thinnest possible principle applicable to all creeds. The Golden Rule stated in the negative: do not do unto others what you would not want others to do unto you, is the result of such a decision.

While a genuine possibility of developing a universally acceptable ethical norm for the global community is encouraging, it falls short of the ideal of human flourishing. What it offers is no more than a passive injunction for survival. Even if such a rule functions well, it is not sufficient to ensure a harmonious community. Many kinds of "thick descriptions" from a variety of spiritual traditions will have to be re-presented. We depend on the concrete manifestations of general principles to live a meaningful life in the world. The need for dialogue among civilizations is obvious.

Ni and Rowe's dialogue is an attempt to reach mutual understanding without losing sight of the full distinctiveness of their means of communication: Chinese calligraphy and English philosophical verse.

Calligraphy was one of the six arts essential for elementary

雖然建立一個能爲世人普遍接受的道德准則的可能性令人感到鼓舞，它却無法企及人的充分發展的理想境界。它所能提供的只是維護生存的消極律令。即便這個律令很有效。它也不足以保證人們會有一種和諧的社團。各種信仰傳統裏的"厚"的成分還是必須要被重新提出的。

史地文的哲理散文詩和倪培民的書法之不對稱的并列是故意的。兩者之間的這種獨特的張力產生出啓人深思和激發靈感的活力。

3

learning in classical Confucian education. The others included ritual, music, archery, charioteering, and arithmetic. For more than a millennium, it has been the paradigmatic mode of self-expression by the Chinese literati. Together with poetry, lute and painting, calligraphy is celebrated as a fine art that strikes a deep sympathetic resonance in the literary mind. Some connoisseurs claim that calligraphy, as one's autograph, is so distinctive that it can very well be characterized as one's own unique voice.

如果哲學如彼爾·哈道 (Pierre Hadot) 所指出的那樣是一種生活的方式，自我的修煉就應當成爲哲學的核心關懷。因爲人之爲人的特點之一是學會如何成爲一個完善的人。這種學習過程包括恒久不斷的精神性的活動。它必然地是一種改變自身的行爲。獲知不只是消極的反映，而且也是行爲。我們無法既真誠地熱愛智慧却又不身體力行地投入益智的過程。

Yet, while voice is natural, calligraphy is cultural.

Surely, *shufa* (the method of writing) originated from observing the phenomenal world and its exquisite aesthetic beauty is achieved by evoking the forces of nature. Calligraphy, however, requires the daily ritual of practice comparable to the most rigorous demands of conventional art. This combining of practice of highly routinized application and highly refined artistic creativity typifies how literati in traditional Chinese society actually lived their ordinary lives. Since they used the brush to write letters, composed poems, draft documents, and record thoughts, calligraphy, as an art, was a natural extension of their social interchange. As the aesthetic value of writing became more consciously appreciated, this personal form of expression obtained great public acknowledgment. The process of writing as well as the final product attracted a great deal of scholarly attention. Ni's calligraphy art, as a result, is both a personal statement and a communal act.

The juxtaposition of Rowe's philosophical verse with Ni's calligraphy is deliberately asymmetrical. The creative tension between them generates an evocative and inspiring dynamism.

If philosophy, as Pierre Hadot characterizes it, is a way of life, self-cultivation ought to be the central concern of philosophy, for a distinctive feature of being human is the commitment to learning to be fully human. Such learning entails ceaseless spiritual exercise. It is necessarily a transformative act; to know is not only to reflect but also to do. We cannot take seriously the task of loving wisdom without personal involvement in the process of learning to be wise. Although modern habits of the heart may have misled us into believing that datum is information, information is knowledge, and knowledge is wisdom, we have not yet lost our ability to listen, to communicate and to practice.

Calligraphy as spiritual self-cultivation is an excellent example of mental and physical exercise. To confront such radical otherness in the English-speaking community could be a liberating experience. The procedure is, however, immensely complicated. We must first become aware of the significance of the other. Only then can we move on to recognition, tolerance and acceptance. With acceptance, dialogue becomes possible. Genuine dialogue leads to reciprocal respect, mutual reference and cross-fertilization.

Rowe and Ni, by inviting us to take part in their joint venture and mutual practice, have helped to move the dialogue to a celebratory act: reaching the universal through the full distinctiveness of cultural forms. Rather than abstracting from the concrete, we can also dig deeply into the lived concreteness of our existence with the hope that the spring beneath will enable us to taste the flowing water shared by others. This experience of sharing may not be generalizable, but it does have universal appeal. We are grateful to them for offering us such an enriching encounter.

通過邀請我們參與他們的合作和交互實踐，史地文和倪培民將上述對話升華到了一種慶典: 他們各自完全地以自己獨特的文化方式而導向了普遍。毋需超出具體去抽象，我們也可以深深地挖掘到自己活生生的個體存在，并有望品嘗那在深層底下流動著的爲他人所共享的甘泉。這種共享的經驗也許是無法成爲共相的，但它却有着普遍的感召力。我們感謝他們兩位爲我們提供了如此寶貴的際遇。

Huston Smith　休斯頓·史密斯

One of the world's leading philosophers of religion and comparative religion, author of the extremely influential The World's Religions, *and most recently of* Why Religion Matters: The Fate of The Human Spirit in An Age of Disbelief.

世界著名的宗教哲學和比較宗教學專家之一，《世界宗教》等巨著的作者。

迄今爲止，東西方對話的工作完全是通過左腦來進行的，也就是說，是通過成串的詞語來表述論點和其他直綫形的思路展開的。我們没有理由去貶損這種形式的對話。從林語堂的《我的國家和我的國人》到諾斯羅普的《東西方的際遇》都表明這種方式的工作成績斐然。類似于《好土地》這樣的小説所起的作用更加值得稱道。但就我所知，此書乃是第一部明確地將執掌空間意識的右腦，通過倪教授那杰出的書法，而帶入到東西方對話中來的著作。

Having myself been born in China and spent my formative years there, I can claim some qualifications for addressing this innovative, hands-across-the-sea book. And I will tip my hand right off. I consider it a courageous, forward-looking venture. Consider the grounds for that assertion:

To begin with, its authors are long-standing friends which gets their project off on the right foot from the start, for friends understand each other in ways that strangers cannot. It is this, more than anything else, I suspect, that enabled the authors to spot an opening for a hitherto untried approach to East-West understanding.

Thus far such undertaking has been sought entirely through the left-brain; which is to say, through words strung together to deliver arguments and other linear lines of thought. There is no reason to disparage this approach. From Lin Yu-tang's *My Country and My People* and F. S. C. Northrup's *Meeting of East and* West, it has accomplished a great deal. And novels such as *The Good Earth* (Pearl Buck was my Mother's closest childhood friend in Chingkiang where the two grew up) have helped; even more. But to my knowledge, this is the first book to bring the right brain - which monitors space and enters this book through Professor Ni's remarkable calligraphy - explicitly into the dialogue.

與印度 — 雅利安文明相比較,中國人的思維方式是具體的。其最明顯的例證是中國象形化的文字。英語文字中沒有任何與中文筆劃的藝術性相似的東西。但就詞語來說,詩詞和它所駕馭的形象是很接近的。

There is another way in which the pioneering approach of this volume can be high-lighted. Compared with the Indo-Aryan civilizations — India's and those of the West — the Chinese mind is concrete. Its pictographic writing offers the clearest evidence of this. Nothing in English script — not even when it is illuminated as in *The book of Kells* - resembles the artistic strokes of Chinese characters, but in words poetry comes closest for the visual imagery it rides; I offer this single example:

Four ducks on a pond,
A grass bank beyond,
White clouds on the wing,
What a little thing
To remember for years,
To remember with tears.

就我而言, 我并没有一下子就進入這個二重奏的意境, 但我被他們的項目所吸引。當我讓自己的注意力在視覺的形象和詩意的構想之間從容地徘徊往返以後, 它的策略開始對我起作用了。

我向倪教授和史教授這一極富獨創性的大膽的嘗試表示敬意!

How far Stephen Rowe's poetry succeeds in connecting with Ni Peimin's calligraphy each reader will decide for himself. Speaking for myself, I was not immediately drawn in to the duet, but as I warmed to their project - slowing down to let my attention swing back and forth between the ocularly visual, on the one hand, and the poetically imagistic on the other, its strategy began to work on me.

So it is that I want to salute Professors Ni and Rowe for pioneering this highly original and venturesome work.

陳佩秋　**Chen Peiqiu**

當代中國著名的書畫家之一
One of the renowned calligrapher-painters in China today

Using calligraphy as a means to engage in dialogue with Western philosophical verses, Mr. Ni is truly a qualified person.

當今書壇，名家林立。然論書者多以筆劃功力，章法布局，字體風格等美學角度評價，書法的修身養性及作爲人生態度之表達、弘揚及交流方式的維度，鮮爲人所關注。倪培民君與史地文君的《筆墨哲思游》一書，以其對人生的深切關懷出發，籍書法與哲理詩爲形式，踐而行之，實爲難能可貴。我對英文散文詩的優劣不敢遑論，觀倪君之書法，則見其于筆墨功力之外，處處透露出他對中華文明之各傳統思想的深刻領悟。其風格之多變，爲書家中所罕見。其能爲此者，乃海納百川，兼蓄并收，而又能各盡其妙用之功也。若論以書法爲東方文明之代表而與西方哲理文字對話，倪君實不辱使命者也。

John B. Cobb, Jr.　約翰 · 科布

A pioneer in the movement to interreligious and intercultural dialogue, author of Beyond Dialogue: Toward A Mutual Tranformation of Christianity and Buddhism, *among many other books, and a founder of The Center for Process Studies in Claremont, California.*

比較宗教學和比較文化學的先驅，《超越對話：邁向基督教和佛教的互相轉化》等許多著作的作者。

The East long ago realized the limitations of rigorously defined concepts and discursive thought. It refused to separate this kind of mental activity from its embeddedness in the life of feeling, action, and imagination. The West pursued discursive reasoning further and with extraordinary success in many spheres. Yet today it finds its very achievements turning into ashes. The unifying visions it once seemed to have attained have fragmented into incoherent academic disciplines. None of these touches the deeper needs

爲了擺脫那走火入魔的理智的統治，西方很多思潮走向了虛無主義。爲此史地文和許多其他西方人士一樣帶着他的激情和痛苦轉向了東方，期望在那裏找到一種沒有异化的生存方式，在那裏思想可以和感情、痛苦與歡樂共存。但和其他西方人不同，史地文將他在西方傳統的根源處所重新發現的生命力帶入了這一對話。

of the human soul. The economics, science, and technology achieved through this process have taken on a life of their own. It seems that they can no longer be bent to genuinely human purposes nor controlled by acts of human will. Enormous intellectual ingenuity is used to show the inadequacy and destructiveness of intellectual ingenuity. At last the recognition to which the East came so long ago is penetrating our Western sensibility as well.

That, too, has its dangers. We have let loose on the world demonic forces that threaten the future of the planet, and the abandonment of discursive thought will not control those forces. But our new humility is also a source of hope. Perhaps we can recover the humanity we have fragmented and lost, and perhaps in that recovery we can gain the strength we need to control our demons. Unfortunately, many of the Western projects that aim to free us from the tyranny of an intellect gone mad only lead us deeper into a fruitless nihilism. For that reason, Stephen Rowe, like many another Westerner, brings his passions and pains to the East, hoping to find there an unalienated way of being, a way in which thought can be at one with sensibility, with suffering, and with joy. Unlike others, however, Rowe also brings to the dialogue a rediscovered vitality at the root of the Western tradition.

With his Chinese colleagues, Rowe has found an other that challenges and enriches. He does not confront the calligraphy that expresses the wholeness of Chinese being with an effort to produce something like that in Western form. There is nothing like that in the West. His verse expresses a distinctively Western struggle with guilt and meaninglessness, as well as the new humility to which I refer. To see how in each case the verse relates distinctively to the calligraphy to which it is juxtaposed requires more insight that I can achieve; aspects of this work remain mysterious. But it is clear that, despite its Western character, it has already assimilated insight from the East, and this insight moves it forward toward the goal of recovering humanity.

Most of our critiques of discursive thought take the form of discursive thought. They call for something they do not offer. In this book we are offered a new way to experience the difference, and the positive connections, between East and West, pushing East-West dialogue beyond ideas and into the dynamics of human transformation. As one deeply steeped in discursive forms, I can recognize the importance of this venture, but I remain grateful for the inclusion of discursive elements that guide me in my response to the art. Perhaps others do not need these crutches in order to move through verse and calligraphy to a new experience of the relation of East and West – and of mutual transformation.

對于推理式思維的批判多半是用推理式思維的方式進行的。它們呼喚那它們自己所不提供的東西。這本書却爲我們提供一種體驗東西方之區別和它們之間的積極聯系的新方式，它把東西方的對話推進到了超觀念領域的，動態的，立人化人的領域。

8

俞吾金　**Yu Wujin**

復旦大學哲學系教授，前系主任，當代中國著名學者之一，著有《思考與超越》
(1986)，《意識形態論》(1993) 等十多部著作及上百篇學術論文。
Professor of Philosophy at Fudan University，one of the leading scholars in China, author of more than ten books and hundreds of papers.

在世界上，有各種各樣的書。放在我們面前的這本書却以其奇特的形式、豐富的内涵吸引着我們的視綫。培民的書法揮灑自如，汪洋恣肆，熔鑄百家而又自出機杼，博采衆長而又自成一格，于字裏行間透顯出深厚的國學旨趣和悠遠的哲學思緒。雖遠居瀛海鯨波之外，却深懷故國喬木之思。Stephen 的詩空靈幽雅，哲思昂揚，融東方西方生命于一身，集實踐、理論智慧于一體。或娓娓道來，如水銀之瀉地；或高屋建瓴，若黄河之决堤。這本奇書真堪謂詩書合璧，相得益彰！

This amazing book is a perfect match of calligraphy and verse. Each brings forth itself by enhancing the other.

許勇翔　**Xu Yongxiang**

中國國家文物鑒定委員會委員
Member of State Cultural Relics Appraisal Committee, China

The calligraphy and the verses in this book are media through which distinctive cultures are embodied and enlivened.

我們常將文物與古董混爲一談。但嚴格説來，文物乃文化的載體，因此古舊的東西，不一定是文物，新的作品，也未嘗不能稱爲文物。文物的價值，歸根到底不在于它的古舊，而在于它所承載的文化爲當代的人們所認可，所珍惜。因此文物的生命在于它的當代性。倪培民的書法和史地文的哲理散文詩，正是它們各自所代表的文化的載體，其背後的傳統文化積澱，通過他們的筆，被賦予了現代感、動態感，成了活的東西，其生命力在他們的對話中得以展現和交融。

Elizabeth Kamarck Minnich　伊莉莎白·密尼克

One of America's foremost feminists and philosophers of education, and author of the seminal book, Transforming Knowledge.
美國著名女性主義哲學和教育哲學家。

S tephen Rowe and Ni Peimin, wishing to communicate with each other across languages, cultures, traditions,

不同的語言、文化、傳統、藝術之間的不可翻譯性没有導致史地文和倪培民的絕望，相反，他們擁抱了這一事實，把它當作通向一個開放的、在中間的王國的邀請。

expressive forms of art, discovered that not everything can be translated-in the usual sense of that term. This discovery, however, did not lead them into the despair of failure. On the contrary: they embraced it, took it to be an invitation to recognize an open space, an in-between, in which meanings are released to play, to evoke, to transcend particularity, even as particularity is honored precisely by the refusal to force it into another form, however (not really) similar...

What their acceptance, their celebration, of what could have been taken to be failure suggests is itself richly evocative and cannot quite be captured. It invites us to think around it, about it, accepting the wisdom of the Jains in India that teaches us we are not wrong in our perceptions of truth, of reality, except when we fall into thinking that any of those moments of illumination suffices unto itself. Rowe and Ni "translate" in the more profound sense of translation as the foundationally relational and transcendent human act.

曹錦清　Cao Jinqing

華東理工大學暨復旦大學哲學與社會學教授，《黄河邊的中國》的作者。
Professor of Philosophy and Sociology, East China University of Science and Technology and Fudan University, author of The China Along Yellow River.

Stepping into Confucianism, Ni's calligraphy shows dignity; settling down into Buddhism, it displays spiritual detachment; diving into Daoism, it wanders freely without constraints and proudly stands above the mundane.

培民是我的大學同窗好友。十余年前，培民赴美留學，繼而在大學任教，專治東西方哲學比較。自1995年以來，每值春夏之際，帶學生來華辦學游歷，積極推進中美民間文化交流。

培民擅書法，廿年前我已知之。今年來滬，出示一集以其友人史地文先生之散文詩爲配襯的書法以賜閱，頓感其書法已入化境，非刮目仰視不足以入其奥堂。入于儒，則其字發爲莊重；沉于佛，則其字顯爲空靈；潛于道，則其字或爲灑脱，或錚錚然透出一股抗俗之傲氣。再觀史君之英文散文詩，初看平淡無奇，了不相干，再讀則若有所發，似有所關，三思而覺其精到發微之處，與培民之書法若即若離，如禪堂應對。人云道不同不相爲謀，何其在不同風格之書法及東西方文字中相與爲謀歟？！培民曰，中華書法，實非單純技巧，而是心靈之修養，人生之踐履。儒道佛各有所長，互補爲用，彰顯出東方人生之智慧。外以彌補西方知性思維之不足，内以調適當代浮躁迷惘之心靈。史君的文字，根源于西方文化超知性的傳統層面，與

The verses and the calligraphy respond to each other with distinct characters and profundities, as happens in a Zen conversation.

儒道佛風格迥异而靈犀相通。故而各自可爲東西方哲理文字際遇之媒介耳。

此書能否承此重任？這是一個仁者見仁，智者見智的問題。培民之書法及史君之文字是否展現其志願，觀賞者自有判斷。而我則視其書而信其言。進而言之，觀其書，則可想見其爲人。值此道德文章裂爲了不相涉兩途的時代，有人力求知行合一，能不令人感奮嗎？

In an era when morality and intellectual life have been split into mutually irrelevant matters everywhere, how could it not be exciting and encouraging to see that there are people actively engaged in unifying knowledge and practice?

Stephen Rowe　史地文

As a Western philosopher, I have come to frustration with traditional ways of speaking. Western Philosophy has been practiced too much in logical argument alone, and not enough in embodied relationship of mutual growth; philosophy has been removed from life by being overly intellectual, abstract, purely mental - rather than providing transformative experiences and humble interpretation that are helpful in the lives we actually live.

Frustration with analytical narrowness and distance led me away from the traditional West and into dialogue with Eastern traditions, feminist projects, and the ecological awareness of our era.

Yet the very same frustration also led me to a rediscovery of Socrates, who stands at the very beginning of Western philosophy. I came to understand a statement from William James that I have carried with me for some decades without knowing exactly why: "Philosophy has been on a false scent since the days of Socrates and Plato." Out of the dialogue mentioned above, I have experienced philosophy as much more than intellectualism, and understood Socrates when he said "the unexamined life is not worth living."

Creating this book with Ni Peimin has been a joyous adventure in learning more effective ways to speak and act. The dialogue with Peimin and his magnificent calligraphy has made it possible for me to communicate and live more directly, more effectively, more spiritually. The calligraphy has led me to writing that is more consistent with the

分析哲學的狹窄及其與實際生活的脱節所引起的失望，使我轉向與東方傳統、女性主義以及當代生態意識的對話，也引導我重新發現了西方哲學源頭上的蘇格拉底把哲學當成幫助真正的"自我"誕生的助產術的傳統。與培民及他的出色的書法的對話，使我能够更直接、更有效、并更有靈氣地生活和交往。他的書法使我的寫作能作爲一種存在的方式，而不只是一種思想的方式，因而更符合蘇格拉底對哲學的理解。

Socratic vision of philosophy as a way of being, not just a way of thinking. It has led me to write philosophy in the mode envisioned by Karl Jaspers when he defined philosophy as "The thought with which or as which I am active as my own self." For, as Socrates said, philosophy, properly practiced, is a midwife – assisting in the birth of "my own self."

Speaking specifically about the verse contained in this volume, it arises from a crucial territory in terms of the human development that is so central to the vitality of our era. In my more discursive work, *Living Philosophy: Remaining Awake And Moving Toward Maturity in Complicated Times*, I refer to this movement in terms of the passage through the psychological and intellectual phases of development, and into the spiritual and historical phases. The point is that the verses in *Wandering* are about and from the same emergence of a new vision of human maturity and consciousness that is coming to be commonly shared in both East and West- and that is crucial to the human future.

Also, a note on translation: in the earlier stages of this project, we worked with the idea that everything could – or should – be translated back and forth between Chinese and English, the calligraphy and the verse. But we discovered, in our own movement to a wider maturity, that translation is not always possible, or desirable. In fact, a world of complete translation into a common (or dominant) language would be a world less rich, less creative, and less interesting than a world in which Chinese remains Chinese and English /American remains its own tongue. Indeed, the genius of "dialogue" in our era is that each language/ culture is not only maintained, but enhanced when it encounters the other in its full distinctiveness.

So readers on both sides of the planet are offered a work in which some parts are translated, some have synopses in the other language, and some parts stand on their own without translation. Even as we learn each others' language, otherness remains, inspiring us in our own continued growth.

Our hope, then, is that this book might be useful in the reader's own development and participation in the goodness of our era. *Wandering* arises from practice, and it is addressed to practice.

我們本來以爲此書中的一切都可以，也應該翻譯成爲另一種語言。但我們逐漸發現翻譯不但有時是不可能的，甚至還是不可取的。事實上，一個被翻譯成一種共同語言的世界，不如一個中文還是中文，英文還是英文的世界那么豐富、有趣、有新意。確實，對話的本質在于代表各種語言和文化的方面以自己完整的獨特性與他方交往時，不僅可以保存自己，而且還能使自己得到增益。

我們的希望是，此書能對讀者自己的發展和參與時代的進步有所裨益。《筆墨哲思游》出于實踐，也是獻給實踐的。

倪培民　**Ni Peimin**

East-West dialogue is a serious and sacred matter,... yet between Stephen and me, it is at the same time a way of relating to each other as ordinary and as cordial as serving each other tea or coffee.

Just as genuine cries and laughs are not created to express feelings, the calligraphy and the verses in this book are not created for the book or any gallery. They are our way of life, our way of relating to each other, and our way of cultivation.

"東西方的對話"是嚴肅而神聖的。書本、刊物、學術研討會，是它理所當然的躋身之處，正像神像理應供奉在神龕裏一樣。但在史地文和我之間，它卻也成了和泡茶、衝咖啡一樣平常、一樣親切的交往方式。我們之間的交流與合作，説成是"一個東方人和一個西方人的對聊"、"對練"，也許更合適些。這不僅僅是因爲"對聊"、"對練"更有世俗感，人情味，而且我總覺得，"對話"似乎在有衝突的雙方之間才有必要，而"對聊"、"對練"才是發生在朋友之間的事。

這本書裏的作品，就是屬于"對聊"、"對練"的産物，而不是正而八經爲"對話"而創作的。史地文和我是同事，在同一個系裏教哲學。平時除了教課、搞學術研究，我們都喜歡塗幾筆。我用中國的毛筆、宣紙寫中文的書法，他用一次性的圓珠筆、草稿紙寫英文的散文詩。他喜歡看我的毛筆字。盡管他不識中文，但他常常先不要我給他翻譯，自己對着那綫條墨塊組成的圖像琢磨。過一兩天，他會遞給我幾行他寫的文字，讓我爲自己的書法所引發出來的聯想而驚奇，而深思，并由此而感覺到繼續提筆蘸墨的衝動。

中國有"字如其人"和"詩言志"的説法。我們的字和詩是我們"人"和"志"的表現。但這麼説還不够，甚至可能會引起誤解。正像真正的歡笑和痛哭不是爲了表現感情而被創造出來的一樣，我們的本意也不是要創作那可以表現我們的字和詩，然后放到畫廊裏去或書本裏去。那字不只是"如"其人，詩也不只是"言"其志，它們直接是我們的生活方式、交往方式、修煉方式。它們是我們的哭，我們的笑，我們的閑言碎語，我們的期冀和浩嘆，我們的互相提示和勉勵。

如今在人們心目中，哲學家往往是玄而又玄、盡講些常人聽不懂也無需懂的詞語的學究。但無論是傳統的東方還是傳統的西方，在其源頭之處，哲學都是對"道"、對完美人生的追求。其最高的境界不只是"知"道，而且是"得"道，與道同一，并能

參與道的造化之功的藝術境界。所"知"之
道要通過修煉而"得"之于身。而修煉不只
是練技法，更主要的是練境界。史地文和我
的"筆墨"之游在互相啓發和促進這種境界
的實現的意義上，可以説是真正的哲學活
動。孟子曰："惟聖人可以踐行"。我等乃不
辭微薄，不甘自弃，願以身試之者而已矣。

Whether in the origin of the traditional East or of the traditional West, philosophy is the search for the Dao, the perfection of life. The highest aim of philosophy is not merely to know the Dao; it is to acquire the Dao, to reach the realm of being one with the Dao, to participate with the Dao in artistic creation. The wandering of our "brush and pen," in the sense of mutual inspiration and transformation toward such a realm, may be considered genuine philosophical activity.

書法與哲理詩

CALLIGRAPHY AND PHILOSOPHICAL VERSES

time forward,
time backward –
it is all in this radiant moment of eternity.
rain on the window in gentle sheets.

雨之舞
Dance of the rain

my real self is emerging also.
growth occurs.
this is the joy and the adventure
of genuine relationship.

發
Develop

sailing at dawn on a fine clear day,
I can then see:
above a city in the distance,
a cloud of - ? pollution,
heat? aura?

see that the same happens to me,
when I awake some mornings in the cloud
of my own - ? dread, guilt?
karma?

on good days I do not identify with
or cling to this condition,
but patiently await the fresh breeze of day.

春眠不覺曉，
處處聞啼鳥。
夜來風雨聲，
花落知多少？
　　　——孟浩然《春曉》

Slumbered away this morning in
　　May, unaware.
Songbirds crying, singing, flying
　　everywhere.
Nighttime came, wind and rain and
　　thunder.
How many flowers fell last night, I
　　wonder?

Spring Morning by Meng Haoran
Translation: Ted Bonarski

千山鳥飛絶，
萬徑人踪滅。
孤舟蓑笠翁，
獨釣寒江雪。
　　　——柳宗元《江雪》

A hundred mountains and no bird,
A thousand paths without a footprint;
A little boat, a bamboo cloak,
An old man fishing in the cold river-
　　snow.

Snowy River by Liu Zongyuan
Translation: Witter Bynner

my mind has no categories
by which to recognize
the benefit of meditation/prayer/contemplation.

modern mind thinks itself far and wide,
but it is dangerously ignorant as to its own source.

stillness, calm, thinking nothing;
accepting without judgment or engagement,
the endless chatter of ego, letting it pass by
(though sometimes we do experience the
enlightenment of pure "Nothingness" – but
we must not attach to this state either).

focus, mantra, and right action are necessary also –
simultaneous with and flowing from that original,
unnamable source.

calm attention.

無
Nothingness

problems-with-self can just as easily be seen as eggwhites:
they nourish the soul in its gradual process
of coming to full presence
on this dangerous and delightful planet.

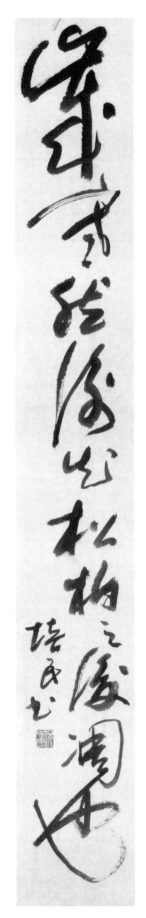

歲寒然後知松柏之後凋也

——孔子

When the cold season comes, it becomes clear that pines and the cypresses are the last to lose their leaves.—Confucius

25

Sometimes it all gets so tight,
Spirit couldn't possibly blow through.
Like rootbound.
Here is where the problem is so bad
I forget I have it.
Hopefully a friend comes along, or some
Fortunate circumstance (often surprising),

And wakes me up, opens me,
Moves me to where the breeze is fresh and
Cleansing.

聽
Listen

I used to be a dialectical thinker:
Beginning with two opposed qualities,
Which are from there resolved in a third.
China teaches me this may not be so.

Before the two is the One,
Which becomes the Third in its full realization.
Now I rediscover the beauty of the West also,
With its great tradition of Thirdness.

Trinity, eternity in the present, Three in One;
We must live this essential paradox before we
Can be a catalyst in the opposition of two.

Only as I begin with the One do I find
Truth unveiled *(aletheia)* in Socratic encounter,
Or Christ present "where two or three are gathered...."

動　Motion

静　Still

How to survive those dead times
that surely do come:
How to somehow throw a bridge across them?

Submit to diagnosis and treatment?
Write a poem?
Go cut wood for a neighbor
with a downed tree limb,
trusting spirit from the bottom of sadness.

長風萬里
Ten thousand miles of consistent wind

"... he restores my soul."
Rebirth occurs, resurrection.
This thought alone could
get me through the night.

"the Kingdom of God is within
you" may also be
translated as "... among you:"
When we are together in a certain way,
"God" is here too.

"thy kingdom come, thy will be done,
on Earth as it is in Heaven."
We should work to help God
join Earth and Heaven.

"When I was a child, I thought like a child ...
but when I became an adult I gave up
childish ways" (while at the same time
"becom[ing] like children").
I have grown; growth is possible;
neither I nor the Earth is complete.
Therefore my limitations and vexations
might be "given up" also.

神
Spirituality

new Shanghai People's Library says:
"Knowledge is Power" (Francis Bacon),
on every floor and in all languages.
visiting the city, I experience a source of power
Bacon had forgotten by the time he spoke –
and set loose the towering language of science.
Shanghai Library garden has oversized
statue of Confucius throwing an inquisitive shadow.

觀 Observe   聽 Listen
思 Think   行 Practice

light in the late afternoon, early fall.
light in a Beech tree, big.
behind and inside leaves and branches,
light shines bright on limbs
like girders in an architectural
construction.
radiating enchantment from the
original order of nature.
here is my own home ground.

言行中和
Let the words and deeds be moderate and harmonious

not trading full
presence tomorrow
for illusion freedom tonight,
yet not failing to dream and cultivate ideals.

雲生大澤
Clouds are generated above big water

One

The way that can be described is not the eternal Way;
The name that can be named is not the eternal Name.
The nameless is the beginning of heaven and earth;
Naming is the mother of ten thousand things.

Therefore ever desireless, one can see the mystery;
Ever desiring, one sees the manifestations.
These two are from the same source but differ in name;
And the source is called darkness.

Darkness within darkness,
The gateway to all mysteries.

Two

When under heaven all know beauty as beauty,
      ugliness is there.
When all know good as good,
      Not-good is implied.

Therefore being and non-being generate each other,
Difficult and easy complement each other,
Long and short contrast each other,
High and low depend on each other,
Voice and sound respond each other,
Ahead and behind follow each other.

Therefore the sage acts by non-action,
and teaches by not saying anything;

Ten thousand things arise and the sage does not reject
them,
He nurtures them, but does not possess them,
And he acts but does not take credit.
When a work is done, he does not claim it.
That is why he will not lose it.

Three

Not praising the worthy prevents contention,
Not esteeming the valuable prevents theft,
Not displaying the desirable prevents anxiety.

The sage therefore rules
By emptying people's minds and filling their cores,
By weakening their ambitions
And strengthening their bones.
He keeps people away from knowledge and desire,
And makes the street-smarts dare not to act.
If no action is taken
Everything falls into place.

Four

The Way is like an empty vessel,
used, but never has to be filled.
Unfathomable, like the source of ten thousand things.
It blunts sharpness, untangles knots,
Soften glares, and calms down noises.
I don't know if it too was the child of something else,
It is prior to the gods.

—Lao Zi *Dao De Jing*
Chapters 1 - 4

道可道，非常道。
名可名，非常名。
無名天地之始；
有名萬物之母。
故常無欲，以觀其妙；
常有欲，以觀其徼。
此兩者，同出而異名，
同謂之玄。
玄之又玄，衆妙之門。

天下皆知美之爲美，斯惡矣。
皆知善之爲善，斯不善矣。
故有無相生，難易相成，
長短相形，高下相傾，
音聲相和，前後相隨。
是以聖人處無爲之事，
行不言之教。
萬物作焉而不辭，
生而不有，爲而不恃，
功成而弗居。
夫唯弗居，是以不去。

不尚賢，使民不爭；
不貴難得之貨，使民不爲盜；
不見可欲，使民心不亂。
是以聖人之治，
虛其心，實其腹，
弱其志，強其骨。
常使民無知無欲。
使夫智者不敢爲也。
無爲，則無不治。

道衝，而用之或不盈。
淵兮，似萬物之宗；
挫其銳，解其紛，
和其光，同其塵。
湛兮，似或存。
吾不知誰之子，
象帝之先。

——《道德經》
第一～第四章

40

道可道非常道名可名非常名無名天地之始有名萬物之母故常無欲以觀其妙常有欲以觀其徼此

兩者同出而異名同謂之玄玄之又玄眾妙之門　天下皆知美之為美斯惡已皆知善之為善

斯不善矣故有無相生難易相成長短相較高下相傾音聲相和前後相隨是以聖人處無為之事

行不言之教萬物作焉而不辭生而不有為而不恃功成而弗居夫唯弗居是以不去　不尚賢

使民不爭不貴難得之貨使民不為盜不見可欲使民心不亂是以聖人之治虛其心實其腹弱其

志強其骨常使民無知無欲使夫智者不敢為也無為則無不治　道沖而用之或不盈淵

兮似萬物之宗挫其銳解其紛和其光同其塵湛兮或存吾不知誰之子象帝之先

久不習小楷撫老子道德經四章以試筆甲戌九七年之秋

most days there are enough flashes of light,
like flying through thick but broken clouds,
to let us know
breakthrough is possible.

contemplating ancient bronze sculpture
in the Shanghai Museum, one in particular
stands out, calls to me:

Fu Yi Gong (Wine Vessel),
Late Shang (13th - 11th century BC),

an artifact of such grace,
a vehicle of such capacity –
similar to the Boeing
airplane that brought me to this place.
my faith is renewed, and I am indeed able to
"complete a ten thousand mile journey
and bring peace to the world."

道
Dao (The Way)

Culture dies when human
relationships are impossible.
People are too busy,
or else too "laid back;"
they are like machines or animals,
too isolated or too close.
The open space of human encounter,
the space in which we may appear and act
in our genuineness is so rare, ironically
despite great riches in physical spaces and vehicles to get there –
physically.
In the rush of materialism,
not enough people notice the extraordinary value
of that non-physical space of human abiding.

What if the Apocalypse is now,
already here,
and it consists, quite simply, in the fact
that people have forgotten how to care for each other;
or they have lost interest?

People just disconnect, and sometimes
you'd not know it.
They give up on any real contact
with others of their species:
too busy, no encouragement,
no practice –
they find machines the more compelling role model.

從容
At ease

everyone here, if they feel at all,
feels depressed:
they feel suppressed and muffled,
thwarted in their humanness.
"alienated" was the old European term,
but it has morphed in America:
everyone feels oppression, and
in the perversity of this culture
we compete for everything, including
victim-rights.

where is that repose from which everything
is a gift?
we must reclaim our humanity,
learn new language of soul.

山不在高，
有僊則名。
水不在深，
有龍則靈。
斯是陋室，
唯吾德馨。
苔痕上階綠，
草色入簾青。
談笑有鴻儒，
往來無白丁。
可以調素琴，
閱金經。
無絲竹之亂耳，
無案牘之勞形。
南陽諸葛廬，
西蜀子雲亭。
孔子云，
何陋之有？

——劉禹錫《陋室銘》

It is not how high the mountain is; if there is an immortal, it will be famous.
It is not how deep the water is; if there is a dragon, it will be divine.
This is a vulgar hut; only my virtue is fragrant.

The traces of the moss are emerald on the porch; the color of the grass is green through the window shades.
Chatting and laughing, all are great scholars; coming and going, none are common folk.
I can strum a pure lute, peruse golden sutras.

There are no strings and woodwinds to confuse the ears; no memoranda or briefs to tire the body.
As the hut of Chu-ke in Nan-Yang; as the pavilion of Yang Hsiung in Western Shu.
Confucius said: Where is the vulgarity?

Inscription on "Vulgar Hut" by Liu Yu-his
Translation: Curtis D. Smith

That mood, an expansiveness tinged
with definite aching, longing,
even mourning, pathos. After what may be several
incarnations, I finally learn
this is my origin.
It is my source, the place in me both most me
and where I open onto the energy of creation – being created
in God's image, as creator: where I myself stand in the draft of
Being.

In a healthy culture I would be taught
how to honor this mood, this strange experience from depth,
the Socratic *aporia*.
I would be offered interpretation, discipline,
authority, companionship in this, in order to let
the extraordinary become the ordinary – in order to become myself.

Without cultivation, that this mood might be felt as wonder and joy
(what else is culture, but this transformation?),
I am terrified by the experience,
run from it, avoid being alone, mislabel it depression or
who knows what, or otherwise numb myself
        from intensity within or without.

氣
Vital Energy

Let it be ordinary, not overwhelmed by your own potential.
no need for that ancient hesitation:

Act beyond this, beyond
the cloud of myself,

Out of and with Nothingness
as source of everything.

Live as a human being.

無爲
Non-action

Who was William James?
He lived as an outsider, never giving himself
Access to the riches he uncovered for others.
Maybe he was a posttraditional Bodhisattva:
One who defers their own movement to enlightenment
For the sake of helping others;
One whose incarnation is the result
Of *karuna* (compassion) rather than those negative energies
(*karma*) that keep us locked in ourselves. Bodhisattva
Knows that *prajna* (wisdom) and *karuna* (love) are the same.
James struggled that we might live;
He generated peace.

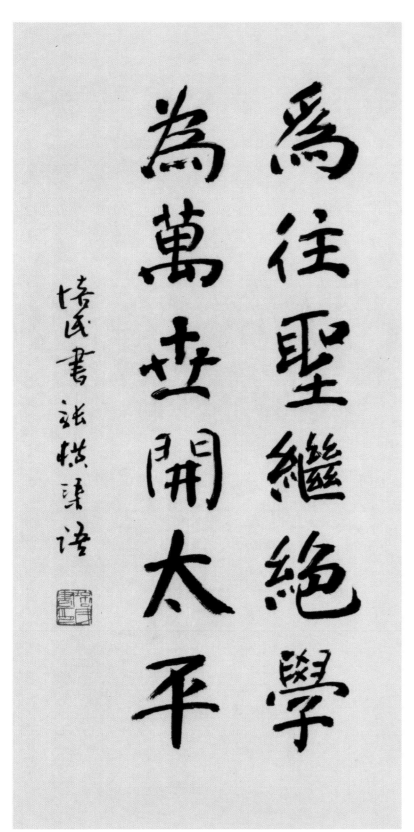

爲往聖繼絕學，
爲萬世開太平。
　　——張載
Carry on the lost schol-
arship of the ancient
sages, generate peace
for the ten-thousand
generations to come.
　　— Zhang Zai

why is China vitalizing?
it is something about history
and the rise and fall of civilizations,
never to be fully stated, except in midnight whisper:
zest, vision, love of the world and
the mutuality of its creation.
something beyond management and psychologies of adjustment,
something about the will of people to be present in their
genuineness.

江北秋陰一半開，晚雲含雨却低回。
青山繚繞疑無路，忽見千帆隱映來。

The autumn darkness covers half the sky
Clouds heavy with rain press low.
Do the blue mountains block all the ways?
Suddenly thousands of sails appear on the horizon.

Translation: Ni P. and Ted Bonarski

Dietrich Bonhoeffer said: "being there for others *is*
experience of the Christ event."

It means being present, real,
alive – *with* the other, not just yes or no.

It is not as simple as either using them or self-sacrifice.
The crucial experience "of Christ" requires sensitivity

to human growth, what the Hebrews called "right relationship,"
community, synergy, love...

the relationship in which we can be Christ to/with each other;
"... no longer I who live, but Christ who lives in me."

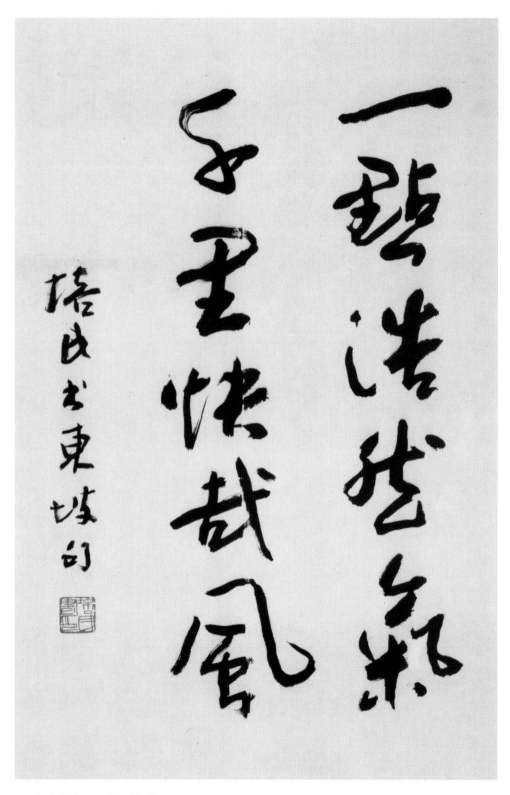

一點浩然氣，千里快哉風

A bit of flood-like qi (vital energy), thousands of miles of pleasant wind.

feelings change,
come and go.
soul does not.

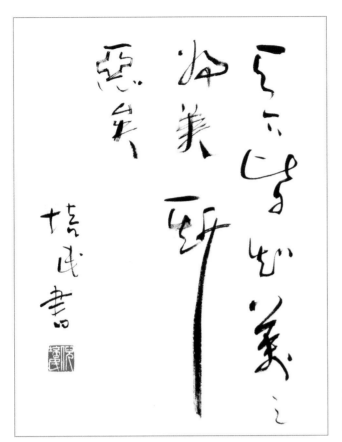

天下皆知美之爲美，斯惡矣。——老子
Under heaven all can see beauty as beauty
only because there is ugliness. —Lao Zi

天地之所以能長久者，以其不自生，故能
長生。——老子
Why do Heaven and Earth last forever?
Because they
do not exist for themselves. —Lao Zi

one advantage of life in community is that
it is much easier to know the
difference between when
you are fully present
and when you are not,
when you are sane and not.

through friendship and personal ties
we come to *Xin* (sincerity, heart)
and real life.

嚶其鳴矣　求其友聲

Song of birds, sound of looking for friends.

Remove clutter, the distraction,
that which disburses and scatters,
eclipses the light. This can only happen when we are
kind to ourselves and our various,
unending limitations.

Calm,
returned,
no urgency or crisis.
Let goodness occur.

Simplify.

删繁就簡　領异標新

Cut redundancy and accept simplicity

Advocate innovation and encourage creativity.

Scapegoat is using the other
as beast of burden
on which to offload from the self
all that cannot be tolerated.

Few are those who can confess
their own limitations.

人貴有自知之明
Knowing about oneself is wisdom

self grows to embrace
many contradictions,
whole realms of ecstasy and sorrow.

self reaches out and thereby empties;
and, in the great tidal movement of
actualization, self gulps life in, a broad range of
possibility, ambiguity, negativity
and inspiration.

this plentitude then
becomes available back to the world,
transformed by conscious awareness
and compassion.
we become co-creators.

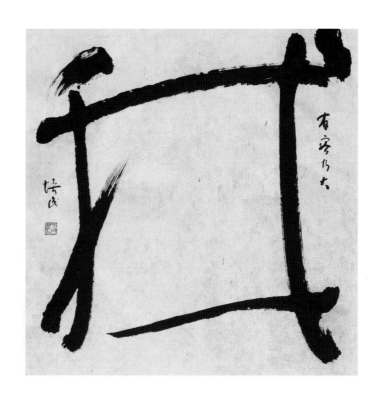

我 —— 有容乃大
I (self) — great when
there is volume inside.

思 —— 思成于悟
Think — Thinking completes
with enlightenment.

大江東去，　浪淘盡，　千古風流人物。
故壘西邊，　人道是，　三國周郎赤壁。
亂石穿空，　驚濤拍岸，　卷起千堆雪。
江山如畫，　一時多少豪杰。

遥想公瑾當年，　小喬初嫁了，　雄姿英發。
羽扇綸巾談笑間，　檣櫓灰飛烟滅。
故國神游，　多情應笑我，　早生華发。
人生如夢，　一樽還酹江月。

　　　　——蘇東坡《赤壁懷古》

The great river flows east,
The waves extinguishing
The debonair characters of a thousand ages.
West of the ancient fortification,
People say, are
The Red Cliffs of the Three Kingdom's Sir Zhou.
Craggy rocks jut into the sky,
Shocking waves slap the banks,
Swirling up thousands of piles of snow.
The river and mountains are as a painting –
Throughout time, how many great heroes ...

Dimly, I think of Gong-jing in those times:
Xiao Qiao had just married him,
Brave valor shown through;
Fan of feathers and bandana of silk,
Among chatting and laughing,
Hulls and masts flew into ash and disappeared into smoke.
My spirit mingles thus in the ancients lands,
Close friends must laugh at me
For growing gray hairs so early.
Life is as a dream;
Pour one cup in libation around the moon in the river.

Cherishing the Past at Red Cliffs by Su Dongpo
Translation: Curtis D. Smith

大江东去，浪淘尽、千古风流人物。故垒西边，人道是、三国周郎赤壁。乱石穿空，惊涛拍岸，卷起千堆雪。江山如画，一时多少豪杰。

遥想公瑾当年，小乔初嫁了，雄姿英发。羽扇纶巾，谈笑间、樯橹灰飞烟灭。故国神游，多情应笑我，早生华发。人生如梦，一尊还酹江月。

东坡词一首　慎民书

69

on foggy mornings, sunrise
comes, like grace itself, from the top down.
it does not come across from horizon.

this phenomenon is something like Zen
"direct enlightenment:"

in this instant of eternity, sunbeams and shadows do not
move slowly across carpeted floors or canyon valleys
as they come into day.
on those magical mornings of clearing fog,
life is fixed in perfection and brightens.

I recall a certain urn in the Forbidden City,
standing out in radiant thusness.

禪
Chan (Zen)

living by grace alone,
morality is no problem, work is a gift,
relationships flourish.

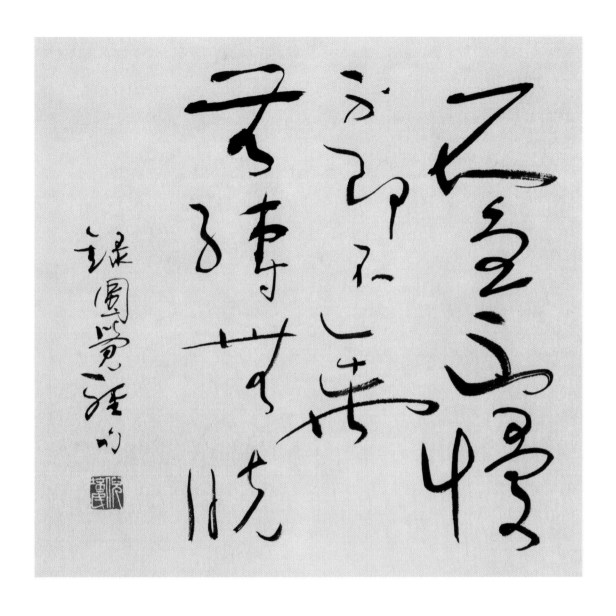

不急不慢，不即不離，無縛無脫　——録《圓覺經》句

Neither hurried nor slow

Neither close nor far away

Neither attached nor detached.

A quote from *The Sutra of Perfect Enlightenment*

That sporting accident,
a crack to myself on smooth cement much
harder than ice:
Shook some sense into me, it did. Here is
what I learned from that event:
No longer will I feel guilty for my life,
my freedom/thriving/pleasure.
(in Greek, *Eudaimonia*; in Chinese, *Xing Fu* –
why is there no clear word in English?)

居安思危
Mind potential dangers when in security.

in the midst of all this –
commitments, questions, my
own sadness –
there is a deep sense of calm and acceptance,
as though it has worked out
just fine already,
living freely, fully, finally

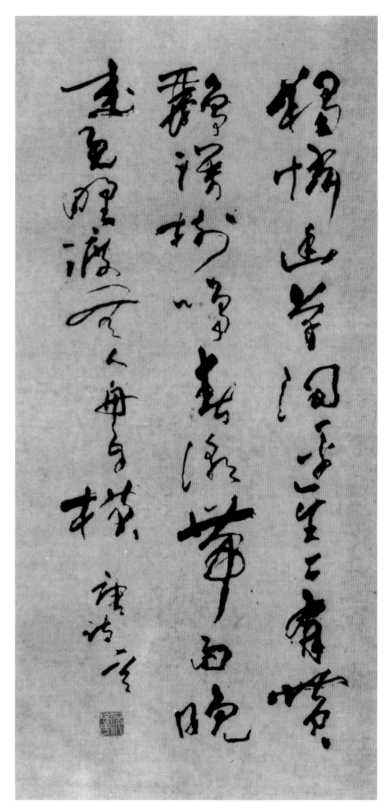

獨憐幽草澗邊生，
上有黃鸝深樹鳴。
春潮帶雨晚來急，
野渡無人舟自橫。
　　——韋應物《滁洲西澗》

Where tender grasses rim the
stream
And deep boughs twill with mango-
birds,
On the spring flood of last night's
rain
The ferry-boat moves as though
someone were poling

West Stream of Chuzhou by Wei Yingwu
Translation: Witter Bynner

指書　Finger calligraphy

We must begin with what is,
with true seeing and objectivity –
with a clear view of what is actual.

A new vision of maturity,
a new human being emerges.

This time, vision does not retreat from life,
touch, the actual –
full immersion in our Earthbound condition:
Objectivity arising from below and in here;
No need for us to be refuges.

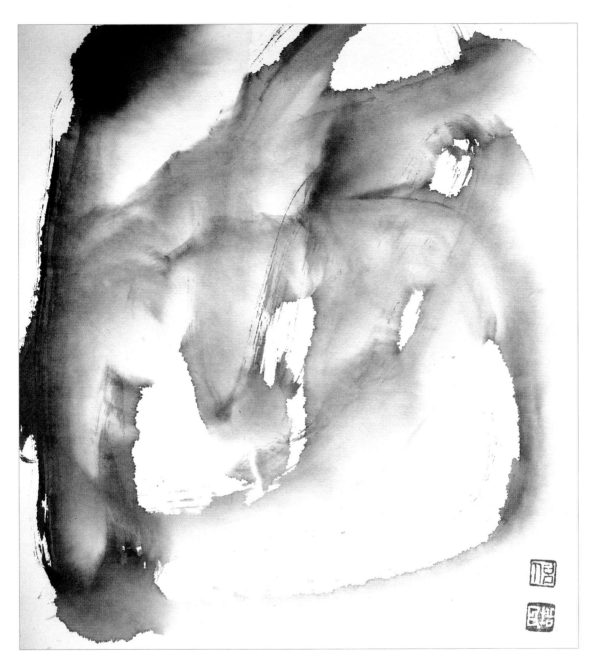

海
Sea

railroad train in the distance,
on a night when the air itself
says snow is coming, amplified by music of the rail,
impending.

what are you doing outside
on a night like this? I am not watching
tv. wind chimes given by a friend
say it too: it will snow in the city.

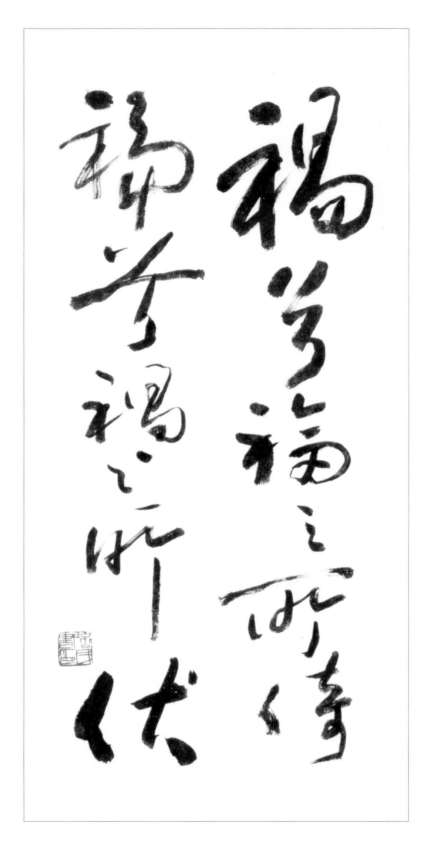

祸兮福之所倚，
福兮祸之所伏。
　　　　——老子
Calamity is that upon
which happiness
depends,
Happiness is that in
which calamity is latent.
　　　　—Lao Zi

In extraordinary moments,
when universal and particular
are simultaneous,
art occurs.
When we respond to those moments,
art is created.
When we appreciate these creations,
we are reminded.
When we live the simultaneity in ordinary life,
we become art.

藝
Art

suchness, thereness,
"whole and against a wide sky" (Rilke).

full definiteness, unprecedented,
as she just is;
not mere potential or projection, need fulfillment or ideal.

actual her eating raspberries at sunset.

peaceful, perfect moment.
there is no threat in change;
everything that happens
is God's plan unfolding in grace.
Yuan Fen.

易、簡

乾以易知，坤以簡能
易簡而天下之理得矣

Change and Simplicity

The creative is known
through change,
The receptive shows in
simplicity.
With the attainment of
change and simplicity
Comes mastery of all
principles under the sky.

the essence of human life
is the drama of response – to the deep,
strong calling; to the urge which is love
and acceptance,
the vitality that will not be named,
Self of self,
God of god.

氣
Vital Energy

作者的解讀

INTERPRETIVE STATEMENTS

MORAL AND PHILOSOPHICAL IMPLICATIONS OF CHINESE CALLIGRAPHY

中國書法的道德和哲學意蘊

Ni Peimin
倪培民

Calligraphy is esteemed as an art universally. Good calligraphy adds beauty to the words and enhances the impact that the words are able to bring to their readers. In East Asian countries such as China, calligraphy is traditionally respected as one of the most highly sophisticated forms of art. The reason that calligraphy can have such a status in China is partly due to the fact that Chinese written language is pictographic and ideographic, rather than alphabetic. In its primordial form, Chinese written language consists of images that picture their referents and directly signify what they mean. That is different from most other languages that consist of alphabetic symbols representing sounds, which in turn are used to refer to objects. The pictorial form allows much more room for the writer to render the written words artistically. The alphabet is limited, and once you begin writing, very soon the repetitiveness of letters is obvious. The number of characters in Chinese written language is in the thousands, which provides much variation. Another important factor is the tools that Chinese later invented for writing – soft brush and

An example of the earliest Chinese written language – bone inscrption.

absorbent rice paper. The strokes written by those tools can be thick or thin, straight or cursive, smooth or rough, the motion can be slow or quick, the ink can be dark or light, wet or dry, the paper can be more or less absorbent. In addition, the structure of the characters and the structure of the whole piece of work can be balanced or out of balance, dull or lively, redundant or succinct – all those permits the artist to fully use her own imagination and creativity. It is like dancing with the soft brush and ink, with the trace of the motion left on paper as a piece of artwork.

中國藝術精神的最高目標和中國傳統哲學的最高目標是一樣的，都是要達到一種天人合一，在參天地之造化中實現自己和實現道的自由境界。

But what is more important in appreciation of Chinese calligraphy is to understand its rich moral and philosophical implications. Speaking about moral and philosophical implications, one might immediately think about the content of a calligraphy work, such as its moral or philosophical teachings, much like the biblical messages written in gothic letters and framed, hung on a wall. It is true that very often Chinese calligraphers like to write moral and philosophical sayings, citations of Buddhist and Daoist scriptures or Confucian classics, but the moral and philosophical implications in Chinese calligraphy are more direct and intrinsic. They are associated directly with images, that is, the brush strokes and the way space is used, not merely derived from the general meaning of the words. Just as one does not necessarily need to know Chinese in order to appreciate the beauty of Chinese calligraphy, one does not have to understand the meaning of the words in order to get into the moral and philosophical implications of the calligraphy.

As the modern Neo-Confucian philosopher Xu Fuguan 徐復觀 plausibly points out, the highest aim of the Chinese aesthetic spirit and the highest aim of Chinese philosophical traditions are the same: to achieve a state of freedom in which the subject enjoys a unity with the Other and is able to move around without obstacle in his or her creative activities as a form of self expression and the expression of the embodied Dao – the Heavenly nature in human (Xu, 1966).

在儒家傳統中，書法作爲六 "藝" 之一，遠非只是爲了藝術欣賞。它具有重要的教化功用。如果一個有教養的人應當知道如何得體地說話和舉手投足，那麼他也應當知道如何像樣地寫字。在較高的層次上講，它和其他五藝都是能使人由生物的人轉化成真正意義的人的途徑，籍此可最終達到 "從心所欲，不逾矩" 的 "游于藝" 的境界。

Confucius has a famous saying regarding arts: "*you yu yi* 游于藝" (*Analects*, 7:6). Wing-Tsit Chan translates it as "Find recreation in the arts" (Chan, 31). Here the word rendered "recreation" is "*you* 游," the same word that the Daoist Zhuangzi used in his "*Xiaoyao You* 逍遥游," where it is typically translated as "wandering." Both translations, "recreation" and "wandering," are inadequate and can be misleading. When Confucius talks about arts, he meant broadly arts and skills, including rituals, music, archery, charioteering, calligraphy, and mathematics – the six arts that constitute the basis of his entire liberal education program. Confucius takes those six arts as much more than how we nowadays understand "recreation or wandering." Confucius says, for instance, "[be] established by the rules of propriety, and perfected by music" (*Analects*, 8:8, Chan, 33). Here music and ritual play important roles in the transformation of a person. "Wandering" is a better translation for "*you*" (and for this reason, we use the word as the title of this book), yet it is still insufficient in explicating the meaning of "*you*." A dictionary that most of our college students nowadays rely on for precise meaning of English words defines the word "wander" to be "to move about without a fixed course, aim, or goal," "to go idly about," "to deviate," or even "to go astray morally" (*Merriam Webster's Collegiate Dictionary*). However, in Confucianism, the word "*you*" means creative activities in which one is able to "follow the heart's will without overstepping or transgressing the line" (*Analects*, 2:4). This is clear from the fact that the above quoted "*you yu yi*" is preceded directly by "Set your will on the Way. Have a firm grasp on virtue. Rely on humanity" (*Analects*, 7:6). The word "*you*," in this context, means a state of freedom achieved by the understanding of the *Dao*, the determination to follow the *Dao*, and ability to participate in the Dao effortlessly and creatively.

(But ironically, the word "*you*" in modern Chinese has also turned toward meaning recreational activities more than meaning creative activities.) A decent handwriting, if one can write at all, was considered by the Confucians part of being a decent human being. Just as an educated person is supposed to know how to talk in a proper manner, an educated person is supposed to be able to write in a decent style. It is not only a matter of respecting what you write, who you are writing for or writing to, and of respecting the writer – yourself, but also a matter of achieving a unity between a person and her heavenly bestowed nature, both in terms of what kind person she should be and what kind of person she is artistically capable of becoming.

Similar analysis applies to Daoism as well. As pointed out by Xu Fuguan, the "*xiaoyao you*" in Zhuangzi is also simultaneously a state of artistic life and a state of being one with the *Dao* (Xu, 1966). When Cook Ding in Zhuangzi's story cut an ox, he did it with a perfect rhythm, effortlessly, as if he was dancing and celebrating. In his performance, there was no opposition

就道家而言，亦如（唐）張懷瓘所說，書“與大道不殊”，（宋）朱長文也說過，“書之至者，妙與道參”。

徐復觀以莊子的庖丁解牛作爲道家藝術境界的寫照，其實還不如以書法來承擔此任。與書法相比，解牛更多地是技巧，而不是藝術的創作。在評論書法時，我們講“情”、“氣”、“神”、“境”、“韵”、“法”、“意”、“風格”、“氣度”等等，評論解牛，何須如此繁復。

between himself and the ox, and no opposition between his will and his hands (his skills). In his eyes there was no ox standing in front of him as an "other," and he was able to "go at it by the spirit" without looking with his eyes. "Perception and understanding have come to a stop and spirit moves where it wants" (Zhuangzi, 46-7). This is a good example of being one with the *Dao*, but not as good an example of the exertion of artistic creativity as calligraphy. Compared to calligraphy, cutting an ox is much more a matter of skill than a matter of artistic creation. Though both cutting an ox in Cook Ding's perfection and good calligraphy require being one with the Dao, the latter is more a participation with the Dao in creation, and the creation shows the artist's own cultivated nature. The aesthetics of Chinese calligraphy is indeed so sophisticated that how much one is able to appreciate it is dependent on the depth of one's own moral and intellectual training. A partial list of the concepts employed in evaluating Chinese calligraphy would be sufficient to show this point: It includes *qing* [mood, emotion], *qi* [energy, vital force], *shen* [spirit], *jing* [realm, standing], *yun* [elegance], *fa* [discipline], *yi* [expressiveness], *fengge* [style], *qidu* [manner], etc. Ox cutting hardly needs so many categories for its evaluation.

From this kind of understanding, Tang Dynasty scholar Zhang Huaiguan 張懷瓘 said that the practice of calligraphy "is no other than the practice of the great *Dao*" (Zhang Huaiguan, *Liu Ti Shu Lun* 《六體書論》), and Song Dynasty Confucian Zhu Changwen 朱長文 said that "When calligraphy reaches its highest perfection, the wonderfulness of it joins the wonderfulness of the *Dao*" (*Xu Shu Duan* 《續書斷》).

Of course Confucians, Daoists, and Buddhists all have different understandings of the Dao, and the differences show in their aesthetic tastes about calligraphy.

For the Confucians the Dao is morally virtuous and the morally virtuous is benevolent, courteous, upright, wise, trustworthy, and follows the golden mean – centrality and commonality. Those characteristics of the Confucian morality determines the Confucian taste in calligraphy. Calligraphy works by Confucians are typically those in which the strokes are solid, with no sharp ends sticking out, indicating their fullness in self-embodiment and no intention to prick others or to show off. The tip of the brush moves always at the middle of the strokes, indicating a sense of righteousness and centrality. Such brush movement

Yan Zhenqing's work shows Confucian characters

顏真卿的書法是儒家風格的典型。寬厚，體諒，正直，穩重。充滿力度而不咄咄逼人，溫雅禮讓而又飽含自信。

method leads to the effect that the marks of the brush are such that when they are thick, they look strong but not swollen, and when they are not thick, they still appear with inner strength and confidence, on the one hand, and no spikiness on the other. The strokes look like a kind gentleman with a broad mind who tolerates, understands, cares, and meanwhile, is full of strength and firmness on principle. Every forward move of the brush is preceded by a backward move as a preparation, and every downward line is completed by a slight withdraw of the tip of the brush. The effect of the strokes will be that they all appear with a proper manner, yielding, polite, gentle, with dignity. The structures of the characters are usually stable, solid, indicating their firm stand on righteousness. They may look a little off the proper balance individually, but that is because they are yielding to each other, so that when you look at the whole picture formed by many words, you find a balance of the whole. This is perfectly in accord with the Confucian principle of propriety, according to which individuals must behave in ways that fit their roles defined by one's social position and relationship with others, and fit the particular circumstances.

The best example of Confucian calligraphy is Yan Zhenqing's 顏真卿. Yan was a devoted official in the Tang dynasty who served the emperor and the country wholeheartedly. At the post of being a governor of Ping Yuan (平原太守), he implemented policies that benefited the people. He showed great courage in leading an army to confront a military rebellion, and even single handedly entered the enemy camp to persuade the rebels to surrender. Eventually, when given the choice between joining the rebels or dying, he chose death with no hesitation.

Yan's calligraphy displays his Confucian characters very well. Fully embodied with moral strength, they are strong, vigorous, but not reckless or robust; they are gentle and reserved, but not inhibited or noncommittal.

The Daoist takes the Dao to be what is natural. They value simplicity and spontaneity. "Doing by not-doing" is probably the best way to express the Daoist ideal

Shimen Song, an example of Daoist calligraphy

《石門頌》反映了道家風格。質樸而韵高，神閑而氣足。如清末書家楊守敬所説"其行筆真如野鶴閑鷗，飄飄欲仙"。

in practice - It is a state in which one is able to do things naturally and spontaneously, with no effort and no arbitrary complication. The Daoist looks for being simple but not self-denial, lively but not bustling, and transcendent but not otherworldly. When such principles are applied in calligraphy, they show preference for less over more, lighter over darker, innocent over articulate, simple over complex. They like the motion of the brush to be as natural as water sliding down from a leaking wall or a stick drawing on sand – this kind of stroke has no arbitrary smoothness, and never appears to be running out of energy.

A good example of Daoist calligraphy is *Shimen Song* 《石門頌》. It is an inscription on rocks, dated back in the Han Dynasty. "The motion of the brush [displayed in *Shimen Song*] is like wild crane and gull in leisure, sleeting like immortals," says the Qing Dynasty scholar Yang Shoujing 楊守敬 (Yang Shoujing, *Ping Bei Ji* 《評碑記》). The strokes look extremely simple and plain, unadorned, almost naive, yet the inner strength and elegance is beyond description. They look reserved, yet everywhere the brush goes it goes with full energy and ease.

A masterpiece of calligraphy that displays both Confucian discipline and also a strong Daoist aroma is *Lan Ting Xu* 《蘭亭序》, written by Wang Xizhi 王羲之 in 353 A.D. The work has been considered the number - one masterpiece in Chinese calligraphy. The original work is lost, allegedly taken to the grave by Emperor Tang Taizhong 唐太宗, as the Emperor loved it so much. What we see today are imitations made by Tang Dynasty calligraphers. The work was a draft of an article about a pleasant gathering together of a group of intellectuals at a scenery spot, with bamboo and water around and mountains and blue sky bathed in a gentle breeze. In a very relaxed mood, and with some wine inside of his stomach, the calligraphy just freely flowed out of Wang Xizhi's hand, displayed an ideal state of being and acting according to the Daoist goal. There were corrections to the text, words added on the side of a line, words that were deleted by a block of ink. All these were kept in the imitations because taking them away would affect the natural beauty of the work. Meanwhile, the naturalness is clearly a cultivated one according to the Confucian

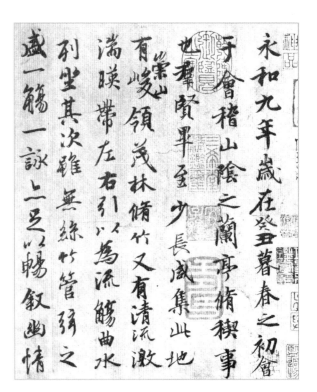

Lan Ting Xu, the "number one masterpiece" in calligraphy, by Wang Xizhi.

96

standard. It displays years of disciplined training and practice. Every stroke, whether a line, a dot, or a turn, follows the proper "*li*" (ritual) so that it starts and ends with a manner, and the strokes all yield to each other and resonate with each other to form a harmonious whole.

The Buddhist takes the Dao to be "Nothingness." According to Buddhism, reality does not consist of "things." All our sufferings come from craving for things that do not exist. We crave for staying young, but there is no eternal youth. We crave for material possessions, but no one can keep them forever. Once we understand this "Nothingness," and are able to live a non-attached life, we can be free from suffering. There are many ways this kind of philosophy can be reflected in calligraphy. One clear example is Li Shutong's case. Li's calligraphy was very handsome before he became a Buddhist monk, just like his own physical appearance. He was extremely talented, capable of being a famous writer, actor, calligrapher, painter, and musician all at the same time. At a young age (38, 1918), when his fame was at the peak, to most people's surprise he renounced his earthly life and became a devoted Buddhist monk. Since then he was known as Hong Yi Fashi 弘一法師 –Master of Great Oneness, and his calligraphy also went through a dramatic transformation. It became less "pretty," less elegant, and less appealing to the popular eyes. It obtained a chilly coldness and simplicity, indicating disinterest in earthly affairs. There are more blank spaces on the works. The characters display little variation, and the strokes move with such a calmness that there is absolutely no anxiety. What is shocking in those works is that they are done by such a talented master, and yet they look so easy going and so "ordinary."

Of course Buddhist philosophy does not have to appear in calligraphy in this particular way. Mi Fu 米芾, Shu Shi 蘇軾 and Huang Tingjian 黃庭堅 were all influenced by Buddhism, yet they had different calligraphy styles. Mi's style is more relaxed, expressive and forthright, Su's style embodies more depth, and Huang's style displays vigor and freedom (See Wang, 9).

Li Shutong's early work, before he became a Buddhist monk.

李叔同早期的書法作品和李叔
同出家皈依佛門後（號弘一法師）
的作品形成鮮明對照。其後期作品
（見下圖）顯示了佛家無執無我，四
大皆空的境界。

97

Li Shuton's later work, after he became a Buddhist monk.

What I said above shows how calligraphy is affected by the calligrapher's philosophy. Yet the causal relation is bi-directional – calligraphy as a practice also affects the person morally and philosophically.

By following the examples of master calligraphers, one learns not only their skills, but also their moral characters and their philosophy! By learning from Yan Zhenqin, for example, one will be affected by his strength, his uprightness, his broadness in mind. Learning from *Shimen* Song, on the other hand, increases one's ability in appreciating simplicity and naturalness. Therefore, selecting which ancient master to imitate is a matter of selecting which philosophy and moral example to follow. People generally advise not to select Zhao Mengfu 趙孟頫 for beginners, that is because his calligraphy is too "pretty." People will be attracted by the pretty appearance and overlook the search for internal strength, discipline, naturalness, transcendence, etc., and easily slip into an evasive, superficial charm that looks like boneless flattery, currying favor with the viewers. That kind of "charm" can be so disgusting that it is worse than natural coarseness. Ming Dynasty scholar Fu Shan 傅山 (1607 - 1684) wrote the following influential aphorisms: "Rather be dull / clumsy than be clever; rather be ugly than be charming; rather be broken than be slippery; rather be straightforward than be arranged" (Fu, *Zuo Zi Shi Er Sun*). He wrote these specifically with Zhao's calligraphy as a reference. He said in the same article that when he was around twenty, he tried to practice calligraphy after all the Jin 晋 and Tang 唐 Dynasties models that were passed on to him from his ancestors. Yet he could not make his works look even close to the models. Then incidentally he got a piece of Zhao Mengfu's calligraphy, and he loved its smooth curves and flowery charm, so he practiced after it. After only a few times, he was able to write in a way almost indistinguishable from Zhao's model. He said: "That is no different from learning how to be a person – when you look after the models of the morally exemplary persons, you feel that it is as hard to be close to them as for a curve to fit a straight line; yet when you go out with gangsters, you will feel that you are closer to them day after day, and very soon you will be no different from them." "Zhao did practice after the

98

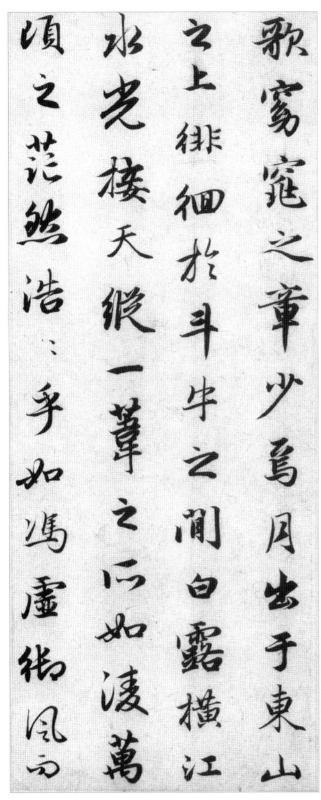

Zhao Mengfu's writing, a style not recommended beginners to follow.

書法既蘊含哲學和道德精神，學習書法自然也就是哲學和道德精神的修煉。選擇書體也就是選擇所要師從的哲學和道德精神的楷模。趙孟頫的字體不適宜于初學書者，就是因爲它那秀逸的外表容易使人追求表面的華麗，忽視內在的修養和功力，從而走向膚淺，詔媚，油滑。

model of Wang Xizhi, yet only because his way of scholarship is not righteous, he swerved to the way of squishy glamour."

There are some other factors that make the process of practicing calligraphy a process of moral education and transformation. Wu Yuru 吴玉如 says, "Practicing calligraphy can help the person to be calm, and through that, make the energy full and the spirit complete. Even a little haste will turn the motion of the brush and the ink entirely different" (See Yang, 4). Strokes cannot be corrected once they are drawn on rice paper. Any correction to the strokes will only make them worse. To the sensitive eyes, even the slightest anxiety or hesitation or the intention to impress others will show up in the work. Calligraphy therefore naturally requires the practitioner to be confident and yet modest, calm and yet full of energy.

99

The practice also helps a person to learn the benefit of discipline. The disciplines in calligraphy are not arbitrary rules. They reflect some natural laws that govern motion and life: for instance, the aforementioned principle that "let every forward move be preceded by a backward move as a preparation, and every downward line be completed by a slight withdraw of the tip of the brush." Just as in order to jump, one needs to bend down first; in order to regain balance after running downhill, one has to lean backward a little. Those are rules one has to learn in the beginning in order to become a master whose brush can dance gracefully and with strong energy that will not easily run out.

The final aim of this kind of learning is to reach a state of freedom where one no longer stands in opposition to the non-self. A person well cultivated through calligraphy should have the confidence, calmness, moral uprightness, and courteousness all embodied in the person as her second nature. When this person is in her calligraphy creativity, she will be truly "with herself" when she forgets the self and when she creates from the non-self.

What I try to show above is that (1) the highest aim of calligraphy, according to the Chinese tradition, is to participate with the Dao in and through artistic creation; (2) philosophical views and moral characters influence one's calligraphy; and that (3) practice in calligraphy helps practitioners in building their moral characters and in the formation of their philosophical positions. However, we must not over-simplify the relationship between moral characters and calligraphy. In the Chinese history quite a few noutorious "bad people" were able to write beautiful calligraphy, for example, Qin Hui 秦檜 (the Southern Song Dynasty prime

書法的道德蘊含不能簡單化地理解。有些歷史上臭名昭著的人也寫得一手好字。如左圖所示宋朝奸臣蔡京的書法就是一例。人不能簡單地以好壞作概論，字所反映的也是整個的個人，而非只是其道德准則。

A calligraphy work by a notoriously "bad person," Cai Jing

minister, who murdered national hero Yue Fei), Cai Jing 蔡京 (also a Song Dynasty official, who would do anything to get into power). On the other hand, some morally exemplary people had just ordinary handwritings. Confucius was never known for his calligraphy, nor were Mencius and many other moral sages.

One way to explain those counter-examples is proposed by Su Shi 蘇軾. Su differentiates the goodness of calligraphy from mere groomed appearance. According to Su, a person with no training in calligraphy would have no skill to write a neat piece of calligraphy work, so the handwriting can be very undisciplined and coarse; yet somewhat in the way that any cell in a person can be used to clone the person because it contains all the genetic information of the person, a calligraphy work contains all philosophical and moral commitments of the person in it. Whether this person is honest, innocent, or righteous, can still show up in the way she writes the strokes. "A man without a righteous mind will inevitably show in his calligraphy some sign of obsequiousness or cruelty" (Su, *Ba Qian Jun Yi Shu Yi Jiao Jing*. The same statement is also seen in his *Shu Tangshi Liujia Shu Hou*).

Su's view quoted above was developed from a broader view which was first clearly stated by Zhang Huaiguan and later by Liu Gongquan 柳公權. Zhang says: "It takes several words for an article to convey an idea, it takes only one character for a calligraphy to display a heart-mind" (*Wenzi Lun*, See Cong, 2). When Liu was asked by emperor Mu Zong 穆宗 about the way to move the brush, he answered "When the heart-mind is upright 正, the brush will be upright" (《新唐書 · 柳公權傳》, see Cong, 2).

But we must be careful here to observe that the state of the heart-mind contains more than just moral qualities. It contains many other aspects of the mind. Bai Jiao 白蕉 calls the sum total of the state of the mind "essence of calligraphy 書髓," which include mood 心境, personality 性情, enchanted elegance 神韵, and aesthetic taste 氣味. Late Qing scholar Yang Shoujing 楊守敬 (1839 - 1915) adds two points to the three points made by another about what is the key to learning calligraphy (natural ability, seeing a lot of good works, and diligent practice): one is to have a supreme moral quality. When one's moral quality is superior one's brush moves with elegance, and will not be fluky. Another is to have rich knowledge. When you have knowledge about thousands of things in your mind, "the *qi* of the volumes 書卷之氣 will naturally fill between the lines" (See Gu, 42). It seems that, while one's moral qualities do affect one's calligraphy, they do not necessarily show up in every stroke, and even if they do they are not often discernible. There is a tremendous room for subjective interpretation and even empathic projection.

Su was in fact aware of the possibility of subjective projection. This awareness shows strangely in a statement that is entirely opposite to what I quoted from him above. He says in that statement, "When one looks at a calligraphy, some people think that one can get information about the person. If that were the case, whether the person is a gentleman or a petty-minded person would surely be displayed in the calligraphy. But that is not the case. One cannot even judge a person from one's

Calligraphy by Mao, the Chinese communist leader.

outlook, how can one judge a person from calligraphy? Sure, when I look at Lu Gong [Yan Zhenqing]'s calligraphy, I would indeed not only see his personality, I would even imagine his graceful demeanor, as if I were seeing him censure Lu Qi and condemn Xi Lie. Why? The reason is the same as Han Fei Zi's 韓非子 story about a man who lost his ax" (*Ba Lugong Tie*). In that story from Han Fei Zi, a man who lost his ax suspected that his neighbor stole it. Every single behavior of that neighbor looked like that of a thief's in his eyes. However, after he found his ax, his neighbor's behaviors all looked perfectly normal. There was no difference between the neighbor's behaviors. The difference was entirely subjective projection.

This view, as it is too extreme, finds little echo in the history. It is as implausible to argue that moral quality of the person has nothing to do with calligraphy as to argue that every stroke in calligraphy shows moral quality of the person. The fact is more likely that though some calligraphy works can be evaluated in terms of moral qualities, some cannot. When one writes in print, the work may simply be neat and nothing else. We may also need to make more careful analysis about different ways in which different moral qualities will affect calligraphy. For instance, petty-mindedness will show up more easily in calligraphy than the lack of care for the value of life, and one who has much good ambition may not differ much in calligraphy from one who has much evil ambition. In the example by Xiong Renwang on the next page, it is hard to imagine that a person with no courage, confidence, and determination can write this piece, and yet it is also hard to judge just exactly how the calligrapher is from this piece of work.

Another related issue is the relationship between moral and aesthetic standards in judging calligraphy.

Su has a view on this issue that deserves attention. He says that "Those who comment on calligraphy in ancient times comment on calligraphers' life as well. If the person was not decent, the calligraphy would not be taken as valuable either" (*Shu Tangshi Liujia Shu Hou*). In other words, moral standard is superior to other standards in judging the

102

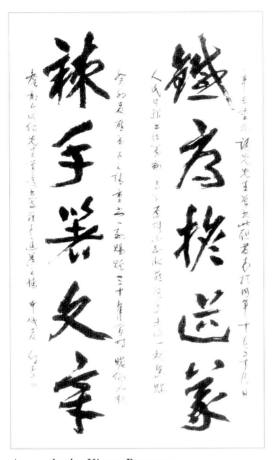

A couplet by Xiong Renwang

人品的有些方面比另一些方面更容易在書法中顯現出來。如上面這幅書法，一個沒有自信、勇氣和決斷的人是決然寫不出這樣的字來的，但僅從這幅字中卻難以看出書者對生命有多愛惜等其他道德品質。

goodness of calligraphy. A groomed piece of work may appear attractive to the eyes but still has no real value. This point is somewhat ambiguous between two more specific interpretations. The first one is that moral standards are different from aesthetic standards. If the person is immoral, his calligraphy works have no value regardless of their aesthetic achievements. This view was supported by Huang Ting Jian 黄庭堅, a contemporary of Su. Indeed, the bad guys are hardly mentioned in the history of calligraphy. Cai Jing 蔡京 was originally considered one of the "Four Great Masters in Northern Song Dynasty" 北宋四大家 (蘇黄米蔡). But his name was later replaced by another person, whose last name was also "Cai" – Cai Xiang 蔡襄, because Cai Jing had a stinky moral reputation. In *On Calligraphy*, Huang writes: "In learning calligraphy one should keep the Dao and Righteousness in mind, and broaden the self by the teachings of the sages. Only then the calligraphy will be valuable. If your spirituality had no discipline, even if you were able to use your brush and ink no less skillfully than Yuanchang 元常(鐘繇) and Yishao 逸少(王羲之), you would still be a vulgar" (See Cong, 2).

The other interpretation is that moral standard is the highest one among aesthetic standards. A calligraphy work that lacks moral goodness in it has a fatal defect in it aesthetically. This interpretation, whether accurate in stating what was truly in Su's mind or not, is more consistent with the traditional Chinese aesthetic spirit. In the Chinese intellectual tradition, aesthetics is never sharply separated from morality. The highest aim of both is one and the same - a state of freedom, in which there is no more separation between the subject and the object, the "heaven" and the "human." In that state, one is able to express one's own heavenly nature in one's own creative activity, and fully enjoy the union. The union between what is heavenly and what is human will show up in the calligraphy works with moral characters; the display of superior moral qualities is itself aesthetically attractive, and therefore deserves the respect as one of the (if not *the*) highest criteria of aesthetic value.

BIBLIOGRAPHY

Chan, Wing-tsit: 1963, *A Source Book in Chinese Philosophy*, Princeton, N.J.: Princeton University Press.

Confucius: 1986, *Lun Yu* 《論語》 [*The Analects*], in *Zhu Zi Ji Cheng* 《諸子集成》, vol. 1, Shanghai: Shanghai Shu Ju 上海書局.

Cong Wenjun 叢文俊: 1996, "'Zi Ru Qi Ren' yu Chuantong Shufa Piping 'Lunli Tuichan Fa' de Yingyong" "字如其人" 與傳統書法批評 "倫理推闡法" 的應用 ["'Calligraphy Resembles the Calligrapher' and the 'Method of Ethical Inference' in Traditional Critics of Calligraphy"]. *Shufa* 《書法》[*Calligraphy*], 96.5. 2-3.

Fu Shan 傅山: "Zuo Zi Shi Er Sun" 作字示兒孫 [Calligraphy Written to Illustrate to Children and Grandchildren]. In *Shuang Hong Kan Ji* 《霜紅龕集》 [*Collected Works of the Shuang Hong Kan*].

Gu Hong 谷鴻: 1997, "Yang Shoujing Shufa Sixiang Guankui" 楊守敬書法思想管窺 [A Preliminary Examination of Yang Shoujing's Thoughts on Calligraphy]. *Shufa* 《書法》 [*Calligraphy*], 97, 4, 41-43.

Huang Tingjian 黃庭堅: *Lun Shu* 論書 [*On Calligraphy*].

Su Shi 蘇軾: "Ba Qian Jun Yi Shu Yi Jiao Jing" 跋錢君倚書遺教經 [Postscript to Mr. Qian Junyi's Handwritten Copy of the Script of Posthumous Advise]. *Su Shi Wen Ji* 《蘇軾文集》[*Collected Works of Su Shi*], Beijing: Zhonghua Shuju（中華書局）, 1969, 2186.

———— "Shu Tangshi Liujia Shu Hou" 書唐氏六家書後 [Postscript to Mr. Tang's Collection of Works by Six Calligraphers]. *Su Shi Wen Ji* 《蘇軾文集》[*Collected Works of Su Shi*], Beijing: Zhonghua Shuju, 1969, 2206.

———— *Ba Lugong Tie* 《跋魯公帖》, [*Postscript for Lu Gong's Model Calligraphy*].

Wang, Xiaoxian 王筱先: 1996, "Qian Lun Chanzong yu Bei Song Shang Yi Sichao" 淺論禪宗與北宋尚意思潮 [On Zen and the Trend of Upholding Expressiveness in the Northern Song Dynasty]. *Shufa Shangping* 《書法賞評》 [*Appraisal and Critic of Calligraphy*], 96.4, 8-11.

Xu, Fuguan 徐復觀: 1966, *Zhongguo Yishu Jingshen* 《中國藝術精神》 [*The Chinese Aesthetic Spirit*]. Taiwan: Zhongyang Shuju 中央書局.

Yang, Luan 楊魯安: 1998, "Tianran Qu Diaoshi – Shufa Yishu Chuangxin Chuyi" 天然去雕飾 — 書法藝術創新芻議 [All Natural without Polish – On Creativity in the Art of Calligraphy]. *Shufa* 《書法》 [*Calligraphy*], 1998, 6.

Yang, Shoujing 楊守敬: *Ping Bei Ji* 《評碑記》 [*Commentaries on Stone Tablets Calligraphy*].

Zhang Huai Guan 張懷瓘: *Liu Ti Shu Lun* 《六體書論》 [*On Six Styles of Calligraphy*].

———— *Wenzi Lun* 《文字論》 [*On Written Language*].

Zhu Changwen 朱長文: *Xu Shu Duan* 《續書斷》 [*Continuation to Judgement on Calligraphy*].

Zhuangzi: 1964, *Chuang Tzu, Basic Writings*, translated by Burton Watson, New York: Columbia Univ. Press.

THE SIGNIFICANCE OF
RELIGION AND PRACTICE
FOR PHILOSOPHY

宗教與實踐對哲學的意義

Stephen Rowe
史地文

*A lecture presented May,
2000 at East China Normal
University shanghai, China*

Today I would like to speak as plainly as possible, and then move to discussion. I do this within the shared vocation of cultivating understanding between peoples through dialogue. The following thought occurred to me when I was preparing for this lecture: the last century was primarily a century of conflictual relationship between governments, while this century could be a century of dialogue between peoples. I hope so, and I want to do everything I can to practice and encourage what we have come to call "dialogue." This lecture, then, is a practice.

I

First, my title: what I want to suggest is that in order for philosophy to be vital, it must be faithful in a practical sort of way to the religious dimension of existence, and that it must be understood and undertaken in relation to all dimensions as praxis – as a way of being and relating of the whole person, rather than just a way of thinking. This understanding has perhaps been commonplace in traditional Chinese philosophy, but it is just beginning to dawn in America.

In this address, then, I would like to speak about the American rediscovery of religion and practice, and do so in the context of a sort of report to you on what is happening in American philosophy today, including a sense of the profound impact and value of Chinese philosophy.

There has emerged in our time a well-known critique of Western philosophy and culture. Tu Weiming says it well:

> Disenchanted with the magic garden
> or universal brotherhood, the
> modern Western intellectual
> overwhelmed by the demands of
> science, technology, and
> professionalism became, as Weber
> acknowledged he himself was,
> unmusical to religious matters and,
> we may add, unmindful of
> particularistic local knowledge.

But the problem is deeper than the Modern/Enlightenment orientation. This orientation is only an intensification of what had been going on in Western culture for centuries. Beginning as early as Aristotle, the West had been dominated by obsession with certainty, abstract knowing, and objective proof. Early on, there set in a strong urge to distance from real life, into the purity and supposed protection of intellectual "first principles."

With Descartes and the beginning of the Modern Period, the distance intensified further. The mind of first principles came to be separated from the body of lived life, including the Earth itself. The body of self and society devolved into the competition of isolated individuals pursuing their "self-interest," understood in terms of material goods, their acquisition, display, and consumption. Meanwhile, "mind" became ever more mathematical, as the instrument of calculation in relation to "interest" in its narrow definition. From our perspective today, it seems obvious as to why the Modern Period in the West would end with themes of alienation, diffuse anxiety, revulsion, and existential revolt.

The dominant philosophical tradition, which both informed and reflected these developments, was finally expressed in the narrowness of the Analytical and Linguistic Movements in the late 19th and 20th Centuries. Philosophy had lost touch with so many people and so much of the joy and sorrow of real life, that even some philosophers began to speak of "the end of philosophy."

The point of this familiar critique of Western philosophy, around which so much of philosophy is active today, is that the dominant forces became overly rational, logocentric, male, and incoherent in terms of life in the world we share as embodied beings. Philosophy even became dangerous sometimes. Witness, for example, Martin Heidegger's relationship with the Nazis.

106

對近現代西方哲學的批評，集中在它的過分理性化，邏輯中心主義，男性化，以及它和眾人以血肉之軀共同享有的現實生活世界的脫節。二十世紀末，西方開始擺脫一元真理觀的束縛，開始放弃真理必須能爲理智的方式所表述的期冀（也開始改變它那據理自傲的態度）。西方開始增進其對話的能力，即在認真對待別的傳統和別的種族的同時，保存和提高自己的尊嚴的能力。

在與中國的對話中，西方人在傳統中國文化最優秀的部分中學到了如何在威廉·詹姆士和杜維明稱作爲"厚的存在"中找到家園，學到了接受物之自然，并在實存的深處發現恬靜，學到了珍惜幸福和以"誠"或"本心"去生活，學到了如何同時變得更加簡單而又更加成熟。我們開始學着進入"通"的境界，并尊重那作爲禮物的生命。在這一切中，我們體會到什么叫修身（學）——那使以上這些品質在日常生活中得以展現的過程。

In my own work of "reconstructing philosophy" (in John Dewey's sense), I suggest that vital philosophy must have three interrelated components, which we can see in earlier the Western philosophy with Socrates: Discourse, Meditation, and Service. In the absence of any of these components, characteristic problems develop. In the case of Western history, when Service and Meditation dropped out, it was more or less inevitable that the Discourse element would drift and be distorted in the direction of dangerous displacement into intellectualism. More on these three components later.

III

Returning to the story of traditional Western philosophy, as the Twentieth Century came to close, the analytical stronghold finally broke up. With release from the thrall of science, notions of cultural superiority, and the need for rigid separation between "philosophy" and "religion," a very exciting, new, and Posttraditional or Postmodern Period has opened up in the West.

The West – no less isolated than the East historically, though in different ways - opened up to the rest of the world, including the worlds of Eastern philosophy, Feminism and Ecology. The West began to move beyond its insistence that there can only be one right answer and that we must claim to have its proper intellectual formulation (and that possession of right doctrine is sufficient claim to superiority). The West began to develop the ability for *dialogue*, meaning the ability to take seriously other traditions (and peoples), while at the same time maintaining and enhancing the integrity of one's own ground.

Initial contact with otherness frequently led to confusion, relativism, cynicism, and a general lowering of human ideals and expectations in the midst of a world of machines and entertainment. But contact also led to identification and appropriation of elements from other traditions that had been lost in our own. Speaking specifically about the dialogue with China, from the best of traditional Chinese culture Westerners have learned how to be at home in what William James and Tu Weiming call the "thick" or depth of existence. We have learned acceptance of what is, and to find repose in and through the depth of the actual. We have learned to appreciate the state of well being (*Xing Fu*), to live with sincerity or "heart" (*Xin*), becoming both more simple and more complex than we had been before. And we have begun to learn how to live with "smoothness" or "throughness" (*Tong*), honoring the gift quality of life. In all of this, we have gained fresh insight into the cultivation of human being (*Xue*) through which these qualities become manifest in ordinary life.

However, we did not simply attempt to *become* Chinese, though this has been a temptation for some, and a typical way in which dialogue has failed in our era - the attempt to become the other. For in the fullness of dialogue there is another crucial element, and that is identification and reappropriation of what is best in one's own tradition, such that contact with otherness has also led to new embodiments of what is truly vital in the West.

IV

What is this greatness of the West?

Briefly stated, there has been a realization that the origin and energy of philosophy lie in a transformative praxis of human encounter, through which we are able to drop our illusions and false knowing, in such a way as to gain greater access to a more profound knowing and living that comes simultaneously from "the religious dimension" and our own genuine self.

The fullness of Socrates' famous statement about "the unexamined life" says it all!

> I tell you that to let no day pass without
> discussing goodness and the other subjects
> about which you hear me talking and
> examining both myself and others is really the
> very best thing that a man [sic] can do and that
> life without this sort of examination is not
> worth living.

Socrates, "Apology"

Hence "philosophy" is a way of living, which includes – but is not limited to – ways of thinking which now can be consciously chosen. As "the very best thing a man [sic] can do," it is relational / associational / communal – in ways that make "Service" absolutely necessary; it is the commonly shared effort to change the world for the better, recalling Socrates' service to Athens. For, as Plato pointed out, the form of community and the form of self are the same. Philosophy also requires "meditation" or the contemplative aspect, as both preparation for the human encounter /

108

relationship that is central to philosophy, and as integration of the growth that occurs through this practice. Meditation teaches us that knowing of genuine self requires more than intellect; it requires silence as much as words. Meditation, including the full meditation of presence with the other in love and justice, means deep listening, recalling the "standing" of Socrates mentioned in the beginning of "The Symposium."

Philosophy as praxis, then, is dialogue with others, including my "self" (the aspect that can be objectified, and the aspect beyond any description). Dialogue entails both "know thyself," and also the kind of openness out of which I can truly hear the other. At the same time, and perhaps more deeply, philosophy as dialogue brings me to the critical state of *aporia* – to the realization that I do not know what I thought I knew, and hence to the "knowing nothing" of Socrates, and finally access to his "inner voice" or "prophetic voice" which "has always been my constant companion, opposing me even in quite trivial things if I was going to take the wrong course." Philosophical practice makes available my own wisdom, conscience, capacity for right action.

哲學，作爲一種行爲或生
活方式，是與“對象”的對話，
包括與那能作爲對象的和不可
言說的自我的對話。對話要求
參與者有自知之明，及那允許
自己真正聽到別的聲音的開放
心態。同時，也許更進一層，
作爲對話的哲學能帶給我們那
“知不知”的蘇格拉底式的智
慧，并最終進入他那如有神喻
的境界。

This way of philosophy – and along with it the Western tradition of liberal education – is not just about information, but transformation. Cultivating the developed human ability to be simultaneously open and definite, to be fully present, this way of philosophy values the distinctively human relationship and what has been called democratic community above all else.

As Plato indicated, philosophy transforms both the individual and community, never one at the expense of the other - as was so often the case in the Western history and social / political thought that followed (alternately emphasizing the individual in ways that harm community, and kinds of community that violate individuals, rarely the democratic relationship in which both are affirmed simultaneously).

V

Concretely in the present, we can see some specific expressions of the Western rediscovery of philosophy. I want to just list four, and give an example or two for each. I think they have all been mentioned above in one way or another, but just for the sake of clarity I will state them here – and fulfill my duty to report to you on "current trends:"

1. Comparison / Relationality: The more creative work is contextual, dialogical, and about some recognizable problem or issue in the world (reflecting Socrates' "goodness and the other subjects about which you hear me talking," i.e.

subjects of real importance). It is "comparative" with a great deal more complexity than had been recognized in the past. The word "dialogue" has come to indicate mutual transformation, replacing an earlier, more shallow comparison of ideas only. In this newer mode of comparison, it is possible to appropriate extremely useful resources from the other, at the same time one becomes more firmly rooted in the integrity of one's own tradition. Here I would especially recommend Hans-Georg Gadamer's monumental *Truth and Method*.

2. Praxis/Practice: Thought and theory have come to be evaluated pragmatically, in terms of their resultant ways of living. I especially appreciate Karl Jaspers' definition of philosophy as "the thought with which or as which I am active as my own self. It is not to be regarded as the objective validity of any sort of knowledge, but as consciousness of being in the world" (*Man In The Modern Age*). I also recommend William James (see my collection of his works in *The Vision of James*).

3. Meditation: Philosophy of Mind or Consciousness Studies has become a very legitimate field in contemporary philosophy, and there is great concern for that humanly possible state of simultaneous calm and focus which has been rediscovered in the West only recently – with much help from the East. In this area I recommend Huston Smith's *Forgotten Truth* and Jacob Needleman's *Time and The Soul*.

4. Service: There is growing interest in "service," understood as the state of simultaneous benefit of both self and other/community, and as the ultimate result and mark of healthy transformation / actualization / growth / enlightenment. Here I would point to Elizabeth Minnich's *Transforming Knowledge*, and Nel Noddings' *Caring*. "Service" is neither "charity" nor mere "self-development," but a *kind* of relationship, a place or space in the world, and the nexus of human vitality.

VI

To share with you even more concretely, I want to conclude by mentioning four specific projects arising in and around our own departmental community in Michigan. These, I hope, represent real embodiments and examples of the new spirit of Western philosophy I seek to describe.

1. Our China Studies Summer Program:
The Director of this program, Peimin Ni, stated the orientation very clearly:

> Comparative philosophy between the East and
> the West has so far focused more on ethics
> and social - political philosophy, and less on
> metaphysics and epistemology, more on
> various problems of philosophy than on
> reflections of different methods of practicing
> philosophy itself, more on narrowly defined
> comparative study – finding similarities and

differences – than on genuine and constructive
dialogue, and finally, not just more, but almost
exclusively, on the theoretical, intellectual
side than on the practical, transformational
side.

This approach, and the "on-site" method with which Professor Ni enacts it, is a model of the broader understanding of philosophy emerging in our time.

2. Service Learning Program:

In our department we have a seminar on service learning that is concerned to clarify "service" and the good it does both us and others. The seminar is based on the radical proposition that if you teach the poor and disadvantaged the "classics" of philosophy and culture from the Traditional Period (West and East), that these people become empowered or entitled in profound ways (deeper than simple satisfaction of "rights"). They – "we" along with them – become capable of developing a democratic personality and living a democratic life.

3. WANDERING:

Professor Ni and I have a joint work, subtitled "Brush and Pen in Philosophical Reflection." Here we attempt a more artful practice of philosophy, Peimin with his Classical Chinese calligraphy, and my writing very short verse pieces in the dialogue with his art. In working toward publication, we have learned that not everything can be translated, and that it is better this way, richer, more interesting, and more supportive of deeper relationship than the conventionalities of any one-language encounter. We have been able to draw strength from each other and our respective traditions at levels deeper than words. With this approach it is possible to deepen dialogue and move closer to lived experience, the actual problems and challenges of life, the real movement to maturity/enlightenment. This work, then, is the fruit of our actual practice of philosophy, both individually and together.

4. Meditation:

In our department we have had special sessions on meditation; some courses address the matter directly or incorporate meditation practice; we have consulted with our University Counseling Center on their offering of workshops on "meditation;" and our new Religion Theme in General Education has "religious practice" as one of its orienting foci. Meditation seeps in from several sources, as an essential resource for healthy, "educated" living, and full engagement of philosophy.

VII

I hope I have shown how religion and practice are at the heart of the Western rediscovery. We are beginning to learn that all components of philosophy, not only the Meditation and Service components, but Discourse as well, must attend to our religious needs and be mindful of positive, practical consequences.

Let me conclude, within the magnificent and magical dialogue of our era, with recalling a statement by Fung Yu-Lan that echoes this same orientation to philosophy from the Chinese side:

> According to Chinese tradition, the study of
> philosophy is not a profession. Everyone
> should study philosophy just as in the West
> every one should go to church. The purpose
> of the study of philosophy is to enable a man
> [or, we might say, "a person"] as a man, to be
> a man, not some particular kind of man.

With this I thank you for your hospitality, and for the richness of our association.